GW00359261

Contents

Introduction

The colour, form and beauty of wild flowers can be appreciated by most people, but an enjoyment of flowers can be greatly enhanced if the observer knows something of their intricate construction and their relationships with one another. Even putting a name to a wild flower can add to its interest and to the satisfaction of the observer. In these respects this book seeks to aid the botanical naturalist.

Unlike most animals, plants are static. This is a real advantage for it means you can examine them in detail without the need of expensive equipment. All you require is a hand-lens (about x10 magnification is ideal) and a whole new world of structure will come into view, from the branching patterns of hairs to the strange topography of the surface of a petal. Often you need to look closely at tiny structures to be sure of your identification, but some plants are quite easy to name at a glance. Removal of parts of a plant (such as leaf or flower) for closer inspection may help your identification but obviously this should be restricted to common and widespread species to ensure you are not harming a plant's prospects of survival. Many plants are protected by law so picking them is illegal. The small format of this book enables you to carry it into the field, enabling you to make identifications without having to collect and remove plants from their natural habitats.

Over 1000 wild-flower species are described and illustrated here; most of the more common and distinct species to be found in northern and western Europe. Those plants which are very scarce or extremely difficult to identify with certainty have not been included, nor have the diverse floras of the Alps and the Mediterranean, for these areas deserve separate books of their own. Once you have mastered the contents of this book you will have a sound basis for extending your knowledge into more complex plant groups and into more exotic floristic regions.

How to use this book

The best way to begin identifying a wild flower is to keep this book closed and examine the plant! It may be tempting to flick through the pictures but this is not the most effective way to achieve accurate identification.

Start with the whole plant. What size is it? Is it erect, creeping or tussock-forming? How are its leaves arranged? What shape and size are they? Are they stalked or hairy? Are the stem leaves different from those at the base? Are the flowers arranged singly or in groups? Now look more closely at the flower and examine a single one in detail (the explanations on pages 4 and 194–5 show plant parts and the ways they can be arranged). How many sepals and petals has it? Are they joined or completely free from one another? Are the sepals hairy? What colour are the petals? How many stamens are there? Are they attached to the petals or to the base of the flower? Now examine the carpels. This may be more difficult for they are often fused in a group – if so, are their styles and stigmas free? It may be helpful to cut a section across the ovary to count the number of cells inside, but let common sense be your guide. Finally note the type of habitat in which the plant is growing, e.g. heathland, roadside or grassland, and any obvious environmental features such as damp or chalky soil.

With all this information you should be able to tackle the key to plant families on pages 4–9; then turn to the pages dealing with the family to which the plant belongs and check against the pictures and descriptions of key features of each species. Do not rely on the illustrations alone; always check that the plant also matches with its "word picture".

Alongside the Latin and English common names of each plant are symbols showing the habitat in which it is most likely to be growing (see p. 194). As plant heights are very variable an average figure is given; the same is true for some plant parts. Unless stated, the measurement refers to the length of the part concerned. To save space abbreviations have been used (see opposite). Technical terms have been kept to a minimum but those used are explained on the inside back cover.

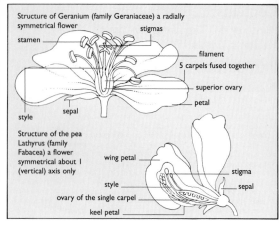

Structure of Geranium (family Geraniaceae) a radially symmetrical flower

stigmas
stamen
filament
5 carpels fused together
superior ovary
petal
style
sepal

Structure of the pea Lathyrus (family Fabacea) a flower symmetrical about 1 (vertical) axis only

wing petal
stigma
style
sepal
ovary of the single carpel
keel petal

Plant key

Work the key by asking questions; each offers 2 (rarely 3) choices, between which you should choose on the basis of your observation (see p. 3). The plant shown here is a test example; it is an erect herb about 50 cm tall with yellow flowers, found growing in wet grassland.

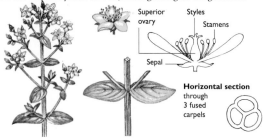

Superior ovary
Styles
Stamens
Sepal

Horizontal section
through 3 fused carpels

The first decision to make from the key is between options **1a** and **1b**, i.e. whether the plant is green or not. The plant is green so go to **2**; it is terrestrial so you proceed to **4**. Now you are asked about the flowers. They are obvious and coloured so you are sent to **5**; there are exactly 5 petals so you choose **5a** and are directed to **6**, where you must choose option **6a**. This leads to **7**. Now a careful check is needed to see if the 5 petals are joined in a tube (even if only near the base). The plant has free (unjoined) petals so you go on to **8** which concerns the shape of the flower. Because the plant has more than one plane of symmetry (i.e., is radially symmetrical), unlike a pea flower, for example, you arrive at **GROUP H**.

GROUP H (p. 7) begins with 3 options, all demanding detailed examination of the ovary. In this plant the flower parts (petals, sepals and stamens) are attached below the ovary so the ovary is superior. There is a single ovary with 3 styles projecting so this suggests 3 fused carpels. A horizontal section cut through the ovary confirms this so you choose **1b** and move to **6**. The plant has many – certainly far more than 10 – stamens so go to **7**. Leaves are in opposite pairs, stipules are absent, so the choice is **7b** which leads to **9**. As already shown there are 3 free styles, suggesting that **9b** is the correct choice. A careful look at the stamens shows them to be joined in groups near their bases, which confirms that the plant is a member of the **Clusiaceae** or **St John's wort family** (pp. 76–7).

Turning to these pages, you will see that members of the Guttiferae vary in such features as growth habit, flower size, hairiness and stem character. Our plant is hairless and has square stems, which confirms it as *Hypericum tetrapterum*, the Square-stemmed St John's wort.

Key to plant groups		Proceed to
1a	Plants with no green parts	Group A (below)
1b	Plants green	2
2a	Growing in water	3
2b	Growing on land	4
3a	Floating aquatics, not rooted in mud	Group B (below)
3b	Aquatics, rooted in mud	Group C (below)
4a	Individual flowers inconspicuous, may be in clusters, e.g., catkins, colour green or brown	Group D (p. 6)
4b	Flowers obvious, coloured	5
5a	5 or more petals or petal-like parts	6
5b	Fewer than 5 petals	10
6a	5 petals	7
6b	6 or more petals	Group L (p. 9)
7a	Petals free (not joined together)	8
7b	Petals joined together	9
8a	Flowers radially symmetrical	Group H (p. 7)
8b	Flowers symmetrical about 1 axis only	Group J (p. 9)
9a	Flowers radially symmetrical	Group I (p. 8)
9b	Flowers symmetrical about 1 axis only, hooded, lipped or spurred	Group K (p. 9)
10a	0, 2 or 3 petals or petal-like parts	Group E (p. 6)
10b	4 petals	11
11a	Petals free	Group F (p. 7)
11b	Petals joined at least at base	Group G (p. 7)

Group A Plants with no green pigment

1a	Plant erect	2
1b	Plant twining around another species	Convolvulaceae p. 105
2	Flowers radially symmetrical drooping	Pyrolaceae p. 92
2b	Flowers not radially symmetrical	3
3b	Flowers 2-lipped, tubular below	Orobanchaceae p. 128
3b	6 free petal-like structures, prominent lower lip	Orchidaceae p. 170

Group B Floating aquatics, not rooted in mud

1a	Plant small (less than 1 cm), disc-like or lobed	Lemnaceae p. 181
1b	Plant larger than 1 cm, not disc-like	2
2a	Leaves finely divided, has small bladders	Lentibulariaceae (*Utricularia*) p.129
2b	Leaves not divided	3
3a	Flowers with 4 petals	Trapaceae p. 80
3b	Flowers with 3 petals	Hydrocharitaceae p.157

Group C Aquatic plants, rooted in mud

1a	Plant erect, tall, emerging from water	2
1b	Plant not erect, usually immersed or floating	7
2a	Flowers conspicuous, individual flowers greater than 1 cm	Butomaceae p. 157 Alismataceae p. 156
2b	Individual flowers small, inconspicuous, but may be in dense, obvious clusters	3
3a	Leaves whorled	Hippuridaceae p. 83
3b	Leaves not whorled	4
4a	Inflorescence surrounded by a sheath (spathe)	Araceae (*Calla*) p. 180
4b	Inflorescence without encircling sheath	5
5a	Inflorescence cylindrical	6
5b	Inflorescence globular	Sparganiaceae p. 181, Eriocaulaceae p. 169
6a	Plant sweet-smelling, inflorescence to one side	Araceae (*Acorus*) p. 180
6b	Plant not scented, inflorescence terminal	Typhaceae p. 181
7a	Flowers conspicuous, white or yellow	8
7b	Flowers inconspicuous, but may be in dense spikes, green or brown	10

8a	Petals free	Nymphaceae p. 27
8b	Petals united	9
9a	Flowers radially symmetrical, white	Menyanthaceae p. 102
9b	Flowers symmetrical about 1 axis only, yellow	Lentibulariaceae (*Utricularia*) p.129
10a	Leaves whorled	Ceratophyllaceae p. 28 Haloragaceae p. 83 Najadaceae p. 159
10b	Lower leaves in opposite pairs	Callitrichaceae p. 109 Najadaceae p. 159 Potamogetonaceae (*Groenlandia*) p. 158
10c	Lower leaves alternate	Zosteraceae p. 158 Potamogetonaceae p. 158 Ruppiaceae p. 159

Group D Terrestrial plants. Flowers inconspicuous, green or brown, but often arranged in prominent clusters

1a	Flowers in catkin-like structures	2
1b	Flowers not in catkins	3
2a	Erect or creeping shrubs	3
2b	Erect herbs or climbers	Salicaceae p. 10 Myricaceae p. 10
3a	Plant parasitic on trees	Viscaceae p. 12
3b	Plant not parasitic on trees	4
4a	Leaves compound	5
4b	Leaves simple	8
4c	Leaves absent, stems cylindrical, succulent	Chenopodiaceae (*Salicornia*) p.16
5a	Flowers in dense heads	6
5b	Flowers not in dense heads	7
6a	Flowers in heads of 5, flowers at right angles to each other	Adoxaceae p. 131
6b	More than 5 flowers per head	Rosaceae p. 50
7a	No petals, 4 stamens	Rosaceae (*Alchemilla*) p. 54 (*Aphanes*) p. 53
7b	4–5 petals, many stamens	Ranunculaceae (*Thalictrum*) p. 34
8a	Inflorescence a dense spike with sheath (spathe)	Araceae p. 180
8b	Not so	9
9a	Milky juice, flowers in umbels	Euphorbiaceae p. 71
9b	No milky juice present, flowers not arranged in umbels	10
10a	Opposite or whorled leaves	11
10b	Alternate leaves	14
11a	Low, creeping stems	12
11b	Plant erect	13
12a	5 sepals and petals	Caryophyllaceae p. 20 Saxifragaceae (*Chrysosplenium*) p. 49
13a	Stinging hairs, 4 stamens	Urticaceae p. 11
13b	No stinging hairs, many stamens	Euphorbiaceae (*Mercurialis*) p. 72
14a	Leaves with sheaths around base	Polygonaceae p. 13
14b	No sheaths at leaf bases	15
15a	Flowers in dense, narrow spikes, leaves linear, not fleshy	Plantaginaceae p. 130 Ranunculaceae (*Myosurus*) p. 34
15b	Flowers not in narrow spikes, often fleshy and/or mealy	Chenopodiaceae p. 18

Group E Terrestrial plants. Flowers conspicuous, 0, 2 or 3 petals

1a	Petals absent, flowers in dense, reddish heads	Rosaceae (*Sanguisorba*) p. 55
1b	Petals present, flowers not in dense heads	2
2a	2 petals	Onagraceae (*Circaea*) p. 81
2b	3 petals	3
3a	Petals joined in a tube	Aristolochiaceae p. 12
3b	Petals free	Alismataceae p. 156

Group F Terrestrial plants. Flowers conspicuous, 4 petals or petal-like parts, not joined together at their base nor in a tube

1a	Leaves undivided	2
1b	Leaves divided into segments	7
2a	More than 8 stamens	Resedaceae p. 44
2b	Less than 8 stamens	3
3a	4 sepals	4
3b	2 sepals, soon falling	Papaveraceae p. 35
4a	Ovary inferior	5
4b	Ovary superior	6
5a	Flowers with large, whitish, petal-like bracts	Cornaceae p. 83
5b	Flowers with true petals	Onagraceae p. 80
6a	Ovary 1-celled	Caryophyllaceae p. 20
6b	Ovary 2-celled	Brassicaceae p. 36
6c	Ovary 5- or 6-celled	Linaceae (*Radiola*) p. 70
7a	More than 8 stamens, leaves palmate-lobed	Rosaceae (*Potentilla erecta*) p. 52
7b	Usually 6 stamens, leaves not palmate	Brassicaceae p. 36

Group G Terrestrial plants. Flowers conspicuous, 4 petals or petal-like parts, joined together at their base, or in a tube

1a	Flowers radially symmetrical	2
1b	Flowers not radially symmetrical	6
2a	Leaves in whorls	3
2b	Leaves not in whorls	4
3a	4 or 5 stamens	Rubiaceae p. 103
3b	8 stamens	Ericaceae p. 93
4a	Leaves opposite, 5 stamens	Gentianaceae p. 99
4b	Leaves alternate, more than 5 stamens	5
5a	Sepals petal-like, no true petals	Thymelaeaceae p. 76
5b	Green sepals and coloured petals present	Ericaceae p. 93
6a	Flowers in dense heads, whorled bracts beneath	Dipsacaceae p. 133
6b	Flowers not in dense heads	7
7a	2 stamens, ovary 1-celled	Papaveraceae (*Fumaria*) p. 36
7b	4 stamens, ovary 2-celled	Scrophulariaceae p. 118

Group H Terrestrial plants. Flowers conspicuous, 5 petals or petal-like parts, not joined together

1a	Ovary superior, carpels free	2
1b	Ovary superior, carpels fused	6
1c	Ovary inferior	21
2a	More than 10 stamens	3
2b	10 or fewer stamens	4
3a	Stipules present	Rosaceae p. 50
3b	Stipules absent	Ranunculaceae p. 28
4a	Succulent (fleshy) leaves	Crassulaceae p. 46
4b	Leaves not succulent	5
5a	Leaves divided into lobes	Rutaceae p. 73, Rosaceae (*Sibbaldia*) p. 53
5b	Leaves not divided into lobes	Polygonaceae p. 13, Ranunculaceae (*Myosurus*) p. 34
6a	More than 10 stamens	7
6b	10 or fewer stamens	10
7a	Leaves alternate, stipules present	8
7b	Leaves opposite, no stipules	9
8a	Leaves palmate, stamens fused in a ring	Malvaceae p. 75
8b	Leaves not palmately lobed, stamens free	Rosaceae p. 50
9a	Single style, stamens free	Cistaceae p. 79
9b	Several styles, stamens in bundles	Clusiaceae p. 76
10a	2 sepals	Portulacaceae p. 19
10b	More than 2 sepals	11
11a	Leaves opposite or whorled	12
11b	Leaves alternate or in a basal rosette	14
12a	Leaves simple, unlobed	13
12b	Leaves palmately or pinnately lobed	Geraniaceae p. 68
13a	Ovary 1-celled	Caryophyllaceae p. 20, Frankeniaceae p. 82

13b Ovary 4–5 celled	Linaceae p. 70
14a Leaves with sticky glands, insectivorous	Droseraceae p. 45
14b Not so	15
15a Leaves with 3 lobes	Oxalidaceae p. 67
15b Not so	16
16a 5 stigmas	17
16b Fewer than 5 stigmas	19
17a Leaves entire (not lobed)	18
17b Leaves pinnate or palmately lobed	Geraniaceae p. 68
18a Many stem leaves present	Linaceae p. 70
18b Leaves confined to basal rosette	Plumbaginaceae p. 99
19a S1 style	Pyrolaceae p. 92
19b 2–4 styles	20
20a 5 stamens alternating with feathery structures	Saxifragaceae (*Parnassiaceae*) p. 50
20b 10 stamens	Saxifragaceae p. 48
21a More than 5 stamens	22
21b 5 stamens, flowers in umbels	23
22a More than 10 stamens	Rosaceae p. 50
22b 10 stamens	Saxifragaceae p. 48
23a Herbs	Apiaceae p. 84
23b Woody climber	Araliaceae p. 84

Group I Terrestrial plants. Flowers conspicuous, 5 petals joined together, radially symmetrical

1a Ovary superior	2
1b Ovary inferior	12
2a 10 stamens	3
2b 5 stamens	5
3a Woody plants, usually evergreen	Ericaceae p. 93
3b Succulent, round-leaved herb	Crassulaceae (*Umbilicus*) p. 47
4a Stamens opposite the petals	5
4b Stamens alternating with the petals	6
5a Single stigma and style	Primulaceae p. 96
5b 5 stigmas	Plumbaginaceae p. 99
6a Leaves opposite	7
6b Leaves alternate	8
7a 2 free carpels with a single style	Apocynaceae p. 102
7b Single ovary with 2 styles or 1 style, 2 stigmas	Gentianaceae p. 99
7c Single ovary and style, 3-lobed stigma	Diapensiaceae p. 91
8a Ovary strongly 4–lobed	Boraginaceae p. 106
8b Not so	9
9a Flowers in a terminal inflorescence	10
9b Flowers axillary or in axillary clusters	11
10a Leaves simple	Scrophulariaceae p. 118
10b Leaves pinnate	Polemoniaceae p. 105
11a Sepals free	Convolvulaceae p. 105
11b Sepals united in a tube	Solanaceae p. 117
12a 8–10 stamens	Ericaceae p. 93
12b 5 or fewer stamens	13
13a Flowers in dense heads	14
13b Flowers not in dense heads	16
14a Stamens completely free	15
14b Stamens united by their anthers into a tube	Asteraceae p. 137
15a 5 stamens, alternate leaves	Campanulaceae p. 134
15b 2 or 4 stamens, opposite leaves	Dipsacaceae p. 133
16a Leaves opposite	17
16b Leaves alternate	19
17a Creeping, with flowers in pairs	Caprifoliaceae (*Linnaea*) p. 132
17b Erect, with small flowers in clusters	18
18a Milky sap, ovary with 2 carpels, 2-celled	Asclepiadaceae p. 102
18b No milky sap, single-celled ovary	Valerianaceae p. 132
19a Twining climber	Cucurbitaceae p. 82
19b Not climbing	Campanulaceae p. 134, Primulaceae (*Samolus*) p. 98

Group J Terrestrial plants. Flowers conspicuous, 5 free petals, but flowers symmetrical about 1 axis only

1a	More than 8 stamens	2
1b	8 or fewer stamens	3
2a	10 stamens, no spur to flower	Fabaceae p. 56
2b	Many stamens, flowers spurred	Ranunculaceae p. 28
3a	5 stamens, flowers spurred	Violaceae p. 78
3b	8 stamens, flowers not spurred	Polygalaceae p. 73

Group K Terrestrial plants. Flowers conspicuous, 5 joined petals, flowers hooded, lipped or spurred, symmetrical about 1 axis

1a	Flowers in dense heads	2
1b	Flowers not in dense heads	3
2a	Leaves opposite	Dipsacaceae p. 133
2b	Leaves alternate	Globulariaceae p. 128
3a	Flowers spurred	4
3b	Flowers not spurred	5
4a	Sticky, insectivorous leaves in rosette	Lentibulariaceae p. 129
4b	Leaves not sticky, present on fleshy stem	Balsaminaceae p. 74
5a	Stamens joined in a tube by their anthers	Campanulaceae (*Lobelia*) p. 136
5b	Stamens free	6
6a	Woody, twining climber, 5 stamens	Caprifoliaceae p. 132
6b	Not a climber, 2 or 4 stamens	7
7a	Ovary 2-celled	Scrophulariaceae p. 118
7b	Ovary 4-celled	Lamiaceae p. 110, Verbenaceae p. 109

Group L Terrestrial plants. Flowers conspicuous, 6 or more petals or petal-like parts

1a	Petals free	2
1b	Petals joined together	14
2a	More than 12 stamens	3
2b	12 or fewer stamens	5
3a	Succulent lvs	Aizoaceae p. 19
3b	Herbaceous lvs	4
4a	Stipules present, clear area round ovary	Rosaceae p. 50
4b	Stipules absent, no clear area round ovary	Ranunculaceae p. 28
5a	Ovary superior	6
5b	Ovary inferior	11
6a	3 stamens (may be joined together)	7
6b	More than 3 stamens	8
7a	Leaves linear, flowers stalked in leaf axils	Empetraceae p. 95
7b	Leaves broad, pointed, stiff, flowers stalked in centre of leaf-like structure	Liliaceae (*Ruscus*) p. 166
8a	Leaves with sticky glands (insectivorous) all in basal rosette	Droseraceae p. 45
8b	Leaves without sticky glands	9
9a	Leaves cylindrical, succulent	Crassulaceae p. 46
9b	Leaves not succulent	10
10a	2 whorls of 3 petal-like parts, no green sepals	Liliaceae p. 159
10b	Single whorl of petals, sepals green	11
11a	Flowers pink or red	Lythraceae p. 82
11b	Flowers yellow/green or white	Resedaceae p. 44
12a	Flowers radially symmetrical	13
12b	Flowers symmetrical about only one axis	Orchidaceae p. 170
13a	6 stamens	Liliaceae p. 167
13b	3 stamens	Iridaceae p. 168
14a	Climber with heart-shaped leaves	Dioscoreaceae p. 169
14b	Not a climber	15
15a	No obvious sepals or sepals petal-like	16
15b	Green, leafy sepals present	19
16a	Flowers in dense heads, surrounded by whorls of bracts	Asteraceae p. 137
16b	Flowers not so arranged	17
17a	Ovary superior	Liliaceae p. 159
17b	Ovary inferior	18
18a	6 stamens	Liliaceae p. 167
18b	3 stamens	Iridaceae p. 168
19a	Stamens opposite petal lobes	Primulaceae p. 96
19b	Stamens alternating with petal lobes	Gentianaceae p. 99

9

Willow family Salicaceae

Deciduous trees and shrubs with simple leaves that often have out-growths (stipules) at their base. Male and female flowers without sepals or petals are in catkins on separate plants.

Dwarf willow	Creeping willow

Salix herbacea — *S. repens*

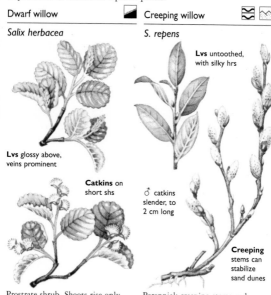

Lvs glossy above, veins prominent

Catkins on short shs

Lvs untoothed, with silky hrs

♂ **catkins** slender, to 2 cm long

Creeping stems can stabilize sand dunes

Prostrate shrub. Shoots rise only 2–3 cm above soil surface. Lvs to 2 cm, rounded, edges toothed. *D:* Fennoscand, Carp; *Fl:* 4–5

Perennial; creeping stems and uprt shs to 1.5 m. Lvs to 4.5 cm and longer than broad; appear before catkins. *D:* N to S Scand; *Fl:* 4–5

Bog myrtle family Myricaceae

Trees and shrubs with aromatic leaves which have no stipules. The flowers have no sepals or petals and are in catkins.

Sweet gale

Myrica gale

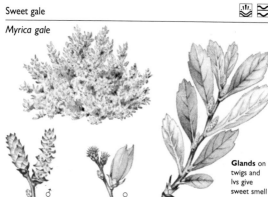

Glands on twigs and lvs give sweet smell

♂

♀

Shrub; male and female catkins on separate plants appear on tips of side shoots before the leaves, which are narrow, downy below and 2–5 cm long. *Ht:* 60–150 cm; *D:* N and W to S Scandinavia; *Fl:* 4–5

Hemp family Cannabaceae

Herbs with lobed leaves which have stipules. Male and female flowers are on separate plants. Stalked male and female flowers have parts in fives. The female flowers are unstalked.

Hop

Humulus lupulus

Fr cone-like, to 5 cm used in brewing

Lvs to 15 cm

♂ **fls** to 5 mm

Woody climber. The square stem is 3–6 m long and twists clockwise. Leaves placed opposite each other have 3–5 lobes and serrate edges. Stem and leaves are roughly hairy. *D:* T; *Fl:* 7–8

Nettle family Urticaceae

Herbs or shrubs, often with stinging hairs. Male and female flowers are in separate catkin-like structures. Flower parts are arranged in fours or fives; the male flowers have 4 or 5 stamens.

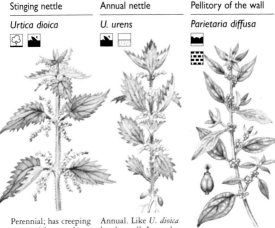

Stinging nettle	Annual nettle	Pellitory of the wall
Urtica dioica	*U. urens*	*Parietaria diffusa*
Perennial; has creeping stems with erect shs at intervals. Stem and lvs have stinging hrs. All lvs have blades longer than stks. *Ht:* to 1.5 m; *D:* T; *Fl:* 6–8	Annual. Like *U. dioica* but less tall. Lower lvs have stks longer than the blades. Each plant has both ♂ and ♀ fls on lfy branches. *Ht:* 45 cm; *D:* T; *Fl:* 6–9	Erect per covered in non-stinging hrs. ♂ fls borne on stem sides, ♀ fls on stem tips. *Ht:* to 1 m; *D:* T; *Fl:* 6–10

Mistletoe family Viscaceae

Woody plants with undivided leaves. They are parasitic on trees but also have green tissues that can function normally. The fruit is a one-seeded berry.

Mistletoe

Viscum album

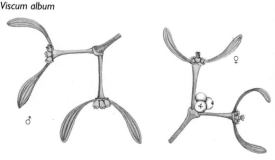

Woody evergreen to 1 m growing on tree branches, especially apple. Stklss ♂ and ♀ fls on separate plants. Leaves 2–8 cm long are opposite each other in pairs. Reputedly an aphrodisiac. *D:* T; (not N or E); *Fl:* 2–4

Birthwort family Aristolochiaceae

Herbs or woody climbers with leaves placed alternately on their stems. The flower parts are three-lobed and arranged in a single whorl. The fruit is a capsule.

Asarabacca

Asarum europaeum

Birthwort

Aristolochia clematitis

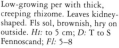

Low-growing per with thick, creeping rhizome. Leaves kidney-shaped. Fls sol, brownish, hry on outside. *Ht:* to 5 cm; *D:* T to S Fennoscand; *Fl:* 5–8

Perennial to 80 cm, distinctive smell. Has creeping rhizome and erect shs on which fls are borne. Fls to 3 cm. Swollen at base. Lvs heart-shaped. *D:* C, S; *Fl:* 6–9

Dock family Polygonaceae

Herbs or shrubs with alternate leaves and sheathing stipules called ochreae. The flower parts, in threes or sixes, persist round the hard, often triangular fruit.

Common sorrel

Rumex acetosa

Erect, hrlss to 1 m. Lvs to 10 cm, downward-pointed lobes at base, upper lvs clasping; fr round. *D:* T; *Fl:* 5–6

Sheep's sorrel

R. acetosella

Erect per to 30 cm. Lvs to 4 cm, basal lobes spreading. Top lvs do not clasp stem. *D:* T; *Fl:* 5–8

Fiddle dock

R. pulcher

Flowers on spread brs that may tangle in fr. Fl parts toothed, fruit 3-warted. *Ht:* 40 cm; *D:* S, W; *Fl:* 7–8

Broad-leaved dock

R. obtusifolius

Erect per. Lvs broad, to 25 cm, hry below; Fl parts toothed, fr 1-warted. *Ht:* 70 cm; *D:* T; *Fl:* 6–10

Wood dock

R. sanguineus

Erect per to 1 m. Brs make acute angles with stem. Fl parts not toothed, 1 wart on fr. *D:* T; *Fl:* 6–8

Golden dock

R. maritimus

Perennial to 50 cm in fr. Persistent, fine-toothed fl parts; fr 3-warted, long stkd. *D:* T (not far N); *Fl:* 6–9

Clustered dock

R. conglomeratus

Upright, brs spread; lf blade longer than stk; ptls untoothed, fr 3-warted. *Ht:* 55 cm; *D:* T (not far N); *Fl:* 7–8

13

Curled dock

Rumex crispus

Erect per. Lvs long, narrow, curled and crisp at the edges. Infl dense, little-branched. Fruit has 3 warts and an edge without obvious teeth. *Ht:* 1 m; *D:* T; *Fl:* 7–9

Marsh dock

R. palustris

Upright ann or bi. 3-warted ft has short, thick stk. Fl parts around fr blunt-tipped with rigid teeth. Plant becomes yellow-brown in fruit. *Ht:* to 1 m; *D:* S, C; *Fl:* 6–9

Water dock

R. hydrolapathum

Robust per; leaves to 1 m. Fruit 3-warted, 6–8 mm long, with triangular segments and a few short teeth. *Ht:* to 2 m; *D:* T (not far N); *Fl:* 7–9

Mountain sorrel

Oxyria digyna

Scottish dock

R. aquaticus

Robust per. Leaves triangular, tapering from base. Lt stks as long as blades. Frs untoothed, unwarted, borne on slender stalks. *Ht:* to 2 m; *D:* C, N, E;

Shore dock

R. rupestris

Erect per. Like *R. conglomeratus* (p 15) but brs almost vertical. Lvs blue-green. Fruit: 3-warted with untoothed margins. *Ht:* to 70 cm: *D:* W; *Fl:* 6–8

Hairless per. Lvs kidney-shaped. Fl and ft stks slender. Outer fl parts spread or bent back. Fruit is broad-winged. *Ht:* 25 cm; *D:* N, C, S; *Fl:* 7–8

Redshank

Persicaria maculosa

Hrlss, branched per. Lvs lance-shaped, often with black blotch. Fl parts lack glands. Fr ridged. *Ht:* to 80 cm; *D:* T; *Fl:* 6–10

Bistort

P. bistorta

Hairless. Lvs narrow abruptly at base to winged stks. Infl dense, to 1.5 cm across. *Ht:* to 50 cm; *D:* C, N (not Scand); *Fl:* 6–8

Alpine bistort

P. vivipara

Creeping, some shoots upright. Lvs taper at base and tip. Fl head often has bulbils at base. *Ht:* to 40 cm; *D:* N, S; *Fl:* 6–8

Amphibious bisort

P. amphibia

Hairless, varies in form. On mud to 75 cm high, in water has floating lvs more tapered at their base. Fl has 5 protruding stamens. *D:* T; *Fl:* 7–9

Knotgrass

P. aviculare

Main-stem lvs longer than branch leaves. Flowers single or in small clusters. *Ht:* to 1 m; *D:* T; *Fl:* 7–10

Pale persicaria

P. lapathifolia

Erect shs often hairy. Lvs to 20 cm may have central blotch. Yellow glands on pale fl parts. Infl dense. *Ht:* to 1 m; *D:* T; *Fl:* 6–10

Water pepper

P. hydropiper

Flowers in slim nodding head have yellow glands. Plant has a burning taste. *Ht:* to 75 cm; *D:* T (not N); *Fl:* 7–9

Buckwheat

Fagopyrum esculentum

Leaves broad, heart-shaped. Fr 2–3 times length of fl parts. Once widely cultivated. *Ht:* to 60 cm. *D:* T (not Fennoscand); *Fl:* 7–8

Black bindweed	Japanese knotweed 
Fallopia convolvulus	*F. japonica*

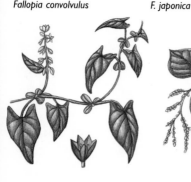

Creeping or climbing annual with twining stems. Fls in groups in lf axils; fr keeled, nut black. *D:* T; *Fl:* 7–10

Upright arching stems in dense clumps. Fls in slender spikes grouped in lf axils. Broad oval, hairless lvs with pointed tips. *Ht:* 1-2 m; *D:* T; *Fl:* 8–9

Goosefoot family Chenopodiaceae

Herbs or shrubs, often with fleshy stems and leaves. Plants look silvery or mealy. Leaves borne alternately have no stipules. The small, simple, greenish flowers have 3–5 lobes.

Nettle-leaved goosefoot	Fat hen
Chenopodium Murale	*C. album*

Angular lvs with coarse, sharp teeth. Infl much-branched. *Ht:* to 70 cm; *D:* T; *Fl:* 7–10

Red goosefoot

C. rubrum

Shining, reddish. Lvs angular with blunt teeth. Flower head dense. *Ht:* 50 cm; *D:* T; *Fl:* 7–9

Variable ann; stems erect, often red-tinged. Lvs dark green or mealy, angular, narrower in infl. Flower parts keeled. Ancient food plant replaced by spinach. *Ht:* to 1 m; *D:* T; *Fl:* 7–10

Stinking goosefoot | Common orache

C. vulvaria

Atriplex patula

Lf stks I cm long

Lvs toothless, pointed
tips. Smells of bad fish.
Ht: 25 cm; *D:* T; *Fl:* 7–9

Many-seeded
goosefoot

C. polyspermum

Leaves oval, toothless;
to 8 cm, not mealy.
Stem 4-angled. *Ht:* to
1 m; *D:* T; *Fl:* 7–10

Erect, branched, mealy ann. Upper lvs linear,
lower have spreading basal lobes. Lfy structures
present around fr. *Ht:* to 90 cm; *D:* T; *Fl:* 9–10

Good King Henry	Babington's orache	Shrubby seablite

Chenopodium
bonus-henricus

Atriplex glabriuscula

Suaeda vera

Upright; dusty-looking
when young. Lvs
triangular to diamond-
shaped. Tapering
terminal infl. Seeds
red-brown. *Ht:* 30–50
cm; *D:* T; *Fl:* 5–7

Prostrate annual like
A. prostrata, but more
mealy. Similar but even
more silvery with
diamond-shaped lvs is
A. laciniata.

Hairless evergreen,
much-branched shrub
with rounded succulent
lvs. Very inconspicuous
fls in axils of upper lvs.
Ht: 1–1.5 m; *D:* W;
Fl: 7–10

Grass-leaved orache

Atriplex littoralis

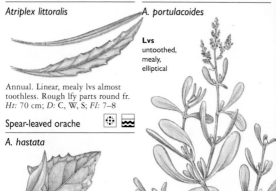

Annual. Linear, mealy lvs almost toothless. Rough lfy parts round fr. *Ht:* 70 cm; *D:* C, W, S; *Fl:* 7–8

Spear-leaved orache

A. hastata

Lower lvs triangular, mealy below; brs more uprt than *A patula*. *Ht:* 80 cm; *D:* T; *Fl:* 8–9

Sea purslane

A. portulacoides

Lvs untoothed, mealy, elliptical

Perennial shrub. Infl dense at sh tips. Fr not stkd. *Ht:* to 1 m; *D:* N to Dk; *Fl:* 7–9

Annual seablite

Suaeda maritima

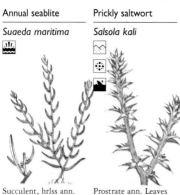

Succulent, hrlss ann. Lvs to 4 cm, narrow, pointed. *Ht:* to 50 cm; *D:* T; *Fl:* 8–10

Glasswort

Salicornia europaea

Fls almost hidden at joints

Succulent ann. Stems and brs segmented, succ. Lvs tiny scales. Edible. *Ht:* 20 cm; *D:* T; *Fl:* 8–9

Prickly saltwort

Salsola kali

Prostrate ann. Leaves unstkd, with spine at tip. *Ht:* to 60 cm; *D:* T; *Fl:* 7–9

Sea beet

Beta vulgaris

Succulent, sprawling, often reddish. Basal lvs hrlss, not toothed, in a rosette. Infl dense, fls green. *Ht:* 1 m; *D:* N to S Scand; *Fl:* 7–9

Purslane family Portulacaceae

Herbs, usually hairless. Flowers have 4–6 petals and two sepals distinguishing them from members of the Pink family.

Blinks

Montia fontana

Fls have 5 ptls, 3 smaller than other 2

Weak, straggling, much-branched herb. Lvs opposite, egg-shaped. Fls in clusters. Spherical fr contains black seeds. *Ht:* to 50 cm; *D:* T; *Fl:* 5–10

Spring beauty   Pink purslane

Claytonia perfoliata   *C. sibirica*

Annual with basal lvs long-stalked but upper lvs completely encircling stem. Fls in groups arise from centre of cup-like lvs. *Ht:* 10–30 cm; *D:* W; *Fl:* 5–7

Annual with basal lvs long-stalked and upper lvs unstalked in opposite pairs but not fused. Fls deeply notched; in open infl. *Ht:* 15–40 cm; *D:* W; *Fl:* 4–7

Dew-plant family Aizoaceae

Procumbent, woody stems with thick succulent lvs, forming carpets.

Hottentot fig

Carpobrotus edulis

Fls 7–10 cm across, usually pink, sometimes yellow. Stems to 3 m; *D:* W; *Fl:* 5–7

Pink family Caryophyllaceae

Herbs with opposite leaves that have no lobes or teeth. Flowers with 4–5 unjoined petals and sepals are in clusters at shoot tips. Petals are often lobed at their tips.

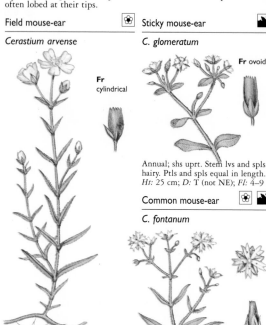

Field mouse-ear

Cerastium arvense

Fr cylindrical

Perennial herb. Brs prostrate to 30 cm. Unstkd, hry lvs to 2 cm. Fls in loose groups. Ptls 2 × length of spls. *D:* T (not far N); *Fl:* 4–8

Sticky mouse-ear

C. glomeratum

Fr ovoid

Annual; shs uprt. Stem lvs and spls hairy. Ptls and spls equal in length. *Ht:* 25 cm; *D:* T (not NE); *Fl:* 4–9

Common mouse-ear

C. fontanum

Creeping hry per. Fl clusters spread out in fr; ptls and spls equal length. *Ht:* 40 cm; *D:* T; *Fl:* 4–9

Little mouse-ear

C. semidecandrum

Erect hairy annual with sticky glands. Bracts have pale border and tip. Infl is loose, especially in fr. Fl has 5 anthers. *Ht:* 1–20 cm; *D:* T except far N; *Fl:* 4–5

| | | | |

Alpine mouse-ear

C. alpinum

Prostrate per. Dense soft hrs on lvs. Ptls 2 × spls. *Ht:* 10 cm; *D:* N, S; *Fl:* 6–8

Sea mouse-ear

C. diffusum

Much-branched ann. Lvs and shs dark green and covered with hrs. Fls to 6 mm with 4 ptls shorter than the 4 spls. *Ht:* 20 cm; *D:* S, W, C, N to Swed. *Fl:* 5–7

Thyme-leaved sandwort

Arenaria serpyllifolia

Leaves hry, pointed, to only 6 mm. Fls 7 mm; ptls notched, shorter than spls. *Ht:* 20 cm; *D:* T; *Fl:* 6–8

Three-nerved sandwort

Moehringia trinervia

Weak ann. Lvs with 3 parallel veins. Fls to 6 mm, ptls shorter than spls. *Ht:* 25 cm; *D:* T; *Fl:* 5–6

Fringed sandwort

Arenaria ciliata

Prostrate hry per. Fls to 1 cm, 3 hry ridges on spls. *Ht:* 6 cm; *D:* T (local); *Fl:* 6–7

Mossy sandwort

Moehringia muscosa

Prostrate hrlss per, 4 ptls 1.5 × length of spls. Fr 4-toothed. *Ht:* 20 cm; *D:* C, S; *Fl:* 6–8

Sea sandwort

Honkenya peploides

Prostrate, succ. Fls to 1 cm among lvs, ♂ and ♀ fls separate. *Ht:* 15 cm; *D:* NW; *Fl:* 5–8

21

Spring sandwort

Minuartia verna

Tufted per. Lvs and spls strongly 3-veined, lf tips pointed. Ptls just longer than spls. *Ht*: 10 cm; *D*: S, W, C; *Fl*: 5–9

Coral necklace

Illecebrum verticillatum

Creeping, hrlss; lvs have oval stipules. Ptls longer than succ spls. *Ht*: 15 cm; *D*: W, C; *Fl*: 7–9

Lesser sea spurrey

Spergularia marina

Creeping brs to 20 cm. Lvs succ, pointed. Blunt ptls shorter than spls, less than 8 stms. *D*: T; *Fl*: 6–8

Mossy cyphel

M. sedoides

Densely tufted per. Cushions to 25 × 8 cm. Lvs succ. Fls 5 mm diam, 5 spls, no ptls. *D*: Scotland, S, E; *Fl*: 6–8

Corn spurrey

Spergula arvensis

Stem has sticky hrs

Annual. Spreading brs from base. Lvs succ, grooved below. *Ht*: 25 cm; *D*: T; *Fl*: 6–8

Sea pearlwort

Sagina maritima

Leaves spineless. Fls on main stem only have 4 spls, no ptls. Many sim spp. *Ht*: 15 cm; *D*: N to S Fin; *Fl*: 5–9

Procumbent pearlwort

Sagina procumbens

Prostrate stems radiating from central rosette. Stems rt at nodes, to form mats. Fls tiny, no ptls. Stems to 20 cm; *D*: T; *Fl*: 5–9

Four-leaved allseed

Polycarpon tetraphyllum

Basal lvs in whorl

Hairless, v branched; lvs oval, upper in opposite prs. Fls have 5 hooked spls. *Ht*: 10 cm; *D*: S, W; *Fl*: 6–7

Knotted pearlwort

S. nodosa

Delicate tufted per. Lvs spined, *c*. 1.5 cm at base, shorter above. Ptls 2 × spl length. *Ht*: 10 cm; *D*: T; *Fl*: 7–9

Smooth rupturewort

Herniaria glabra

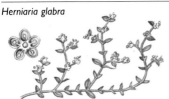

Prostrate, hrlss. Lvs opposite, to 1 cm long with stipules. Fls in dense clusters each 2 mm diam, 5 tiny ptls. *Ht:* 15 cm; *D:* T (not far N); *Fl:* 7

Marsh stitchwort

S. palustris

Creeping perennial. Untoothed lvs. Bracts have green stripe. Ptls deeply cleft. *Ht:* 40 cm; *D:* N, C; *Fl:* 5–7

Greater stitchwort

S. holostea

Stems brittle, uprt, 4-angled. Lvs rough. Fls to 3 cm, ptls cut to half length, 10 stms, 3 styles. *Ht:* 45 cm; *D:* T (not far N); *Fl:* 4–6

Lesser stitchwort

S. graminea

Leaves toothless, hry at base. Colourless bracts. Fls to 1.2 cm, ptls and spls equal. *Ht:* 50 cm; *D:* T; *Fl:* 5–8

Upright chickweed

Moenchia erecta

Perennial; erect stem to 12 cm. Lvs hairless, longest below. Fls to 8 mm, spls longer than ptls. *D:* W, C, N to Eng; *Fl:* 5–6

Common chickweed

Stellaria media

Weak ann. Stems have 1 line of hrs between lf pairs. Ptls cleft. Fr 6-lobed. *Ht:* to 40 cm; *D:* T; *Fl:* 1–12

Water chickweed

Myosoton aquaticum

Weak, spreading per. Shs to 1 m, hry above. Upper lvs unstkd; fls to 1.5 cm, lobed ptls 1.5 × spls. *D:* T (not far N); *Fl:* 7–8

23

White campion

Silene latifolia

Shoots erect, hry. Lvs hry, to 10 cm, upper lvs unstkd. Fls to 3 cm, spls a tube. Separate ♂ and ♀ plants. *Ht:* 60 cm; *D:* T; *Fl:* 5–9

Bladder campion

S. vulgaris

Branched per. Upper lvs unstkd, blue-green. Infl much-branched with inflated spl tube and colourless bracts. Fls to 1.8 cm. *Ht:* 60 cm; *D:* T; *Fl:* 6–8

Red campion

S. dioica

Like *S. latifolia*. Stems hry. Winged stks on basal lvs. Teeth on fr curled back. *Ht:* 60 cm; *D:* T; *Fl:* 5–6

White sticky catchfly

S. viscosa

Basal lvs have wavy edges

Plant covered in dense, sticky hrs. Infl looks whorled. Ptls lobed. *Ht:* to 60 cm; *D:* C, E; *Fl:* 6–7

Northern catchfly

S. wahlbergella

Unbranched per, less than 30 cm. Ptls just outside swollen spl tube. *D:* Arct; *Fl:* 6–8

Sand catchfly

S. conica

Very sticky, hry ann. Fl to 5 mm, spl tube hry, conical. *Ht:* 25 cm; *D:* C, S; *Fl:* 5–8

Forked catchfly

S. dichotoma

Stems hry. Branched infl, 5–10 fls per br. Spl tube hry. *Ht:* 60 cm; *D:* E; *Fl:* 5–8

Spanish catchfly

S. otites

Sticky hrs on stem. Basal lvs spathulate. Many 4 mm fls in infl, spl tube hrlss. ♂ and ♀ separate. *Ht:* 55 cm; *D:* C, S, E; *Fl:* 6–9

Nottingham catchfly

S. nutans

Perennial; erect shoots have sticky hrs above. Lvs hry, basal lvs long-stkd. Ptls narrow, v cut, lobes inrolled. *Ht:* 60 cm; *D:* T; *Fl:* 5–7

Sea campion

S. uniflora

Cushion-forming. Lvs stiff. Fls 2.5 cm, 4 per infl. Bracts lf-like. Fr 6-toothed. *Ht:* 15 cm; *D:* W; *Fl:* 6–8

Rock catchfly

S. rupestris

Short per; lvs narrow. Infl spread, fls long-stkd, ptls notched but not deeply lobed. *Ht:* 15 cm; *D:* Fennoscand, W, C; *Fl:* 6–9

Moss campion

S. acaulis

Cushion-forming. Lvs v narrow, in rosettes. Fls single to 1.2 cm. Spl tube often reddish, wider at mouth. *Ht:* 8 cm; *D:* Arct, C, W; *Fl:* 7–8

Creeping gypsophila

Gypsophila repens

Creeping hrlss per. Up to 30 fls in infl, fl stks 2 × length of spl tube, 2 styles. *Ht:* 20 cm; *D:* C; *Fl:* 6–9

Annual gypsophila

G. muralis

Very branched ann, hrlss above. Infl loose, fls to 4 mm, ptls 2 × spl length. *Ht:* 20 cm; *D:* C, E; *Fl:* 6–10

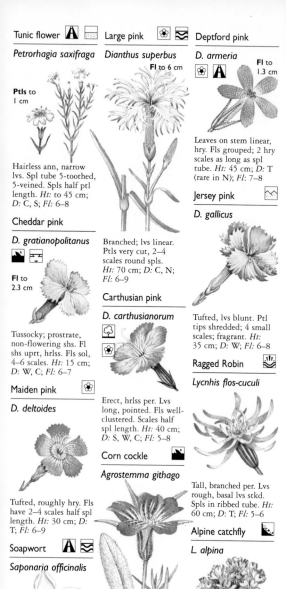

Tunic flower

Petrorhagia saxifraga

Ptls to 1 cm

Hairless ann, narrow lvs. Spl tube 5-toothed, 5-veined. Spls half ptl length. *Ht:* to 45 cm; *D:* C, S; *Fl:* 6–8

Cheddar pink

D. gratianopolitanus

Fl to 2.3 cm

Tussocky; prostrate, non-flowering shs. Fl shs uprt, hrlss. Fls sol, 4–6 scales. *Ht:* 15 cm; *D:* W, C; *Fl:* 6–7

Maiden pink

D. deltoides

Tufted, roughly hry. Fls have 2–4 scales half spl length. *Ht:* 30 cm; *D:* T; *Fl:* 6–9

Soapwort

Saponaria officinalis

Hairless lvs to 10 cm. Infl dense, no scales below spls. *Ht:* 60 cm; *D:* T (not N); *Fl:* 7–9

Large pink

Dianthus superbus

Fl to 6 cm

Branched; lvs linear. Ptls very cut, 2–4 scales round spls. *Ht:* 70 cm; *D:* C, N; *Fl:* 6–9

Carthusian pink

D. carthusianorum

Erect, hrlss per. Lvs long, pointed. Fls well-clustered. Scales half spl length. *Ht:* 40 cm; *D:* S, W, C; *Fl:* 5–8

Corn cockle

Agrostemma githago

Unbranched stem and fl stks have white hrs. Spls long, pointed. *Ht:* to 1 m; *D:* S; *Fl:* 6–8

Deptford pink

D. armeria

Fl to 1.3 cm

Leaves on stem linear, hry. Fls grouped; 2 hry scales as long as spl tube. *Ht:* 45 cm; *D:* T (rare in N); *Fl:* 7–8

Jersey pink

D. gallicus

Tufted, lvs blunt. Ptl tips shredded; 4 small scales; fragrant. *Ht:* 35 cm; *D:* W; *Fl:* 6–8

Ragged Robin

Lycnhis flos-cuculi

Tall, branched per. Lvs rough, basal lvs stkd. Spls in ribbed tube. *Ht:* 60 cm; *D:* T; *Fl:* 5–6

Alpine catchfly

L. alpina

Leaves in basal rosette. Dense infl of *c.* 20 fls, ptls 2-lobed. *Ht:* 10 cm; *D:* N, S; *Fl:* 6–7

Sticky catchfly		Flower of Jove

L. viscaria

L. flos-jovis

Sticky hrs on upper stem. Infl of 3–6 short-stkd fls, ptls notched, spl tube long. *Ht:* 60 cm; *D:* T; *Fl:* 5–6

Branched per. Long-stkd fls in flat-topped infl. Ptls to 1 cm, deeply 2-lobed. *Ht:* 60 cm; *D:* C; *Fl:* 6–8

Annual knawel	Night-flowering catchfly

Scleranthus annus

Silene noctiflora

Linear lvs in opposite pairs. Prostrate or upright stems. Fls green and inconspicuous. Sepals have pale border. *Ht:* 5–20 cm; *D:* T; *Fl:* 6–8

Erect ann with sticky, glandular, hry stems and lvs. Few fls in infl, deeply lobed ptls often curling inwards. 3 styles. *Ht:* 15–50 cm; *D:* T; *Fl:* 7–9

Water-lily family Nymphaceae

Perennial aquatics with submerged rhizomes and floating leaves. Single flowers have 3–6 sepals and 3 or more petals.

White water lily	Yellow water lily

Nymphaea alba

Nuphar lutea

Circular floating lvs to 30 cm across, deeply cleft at attachment to lf stk. Fls are up to 20 cm across and have 4 spls and many ptls. *D:* T; *Fl:* 7–8

Floating lvs oval, to 40 cm across, cleft at base. Fls to 6 cm, raised above water, have 5–6 spls and many ptls a third of spl length. *D:* T; *Fl:* 7–8

27

Hornwort family Ceratophyllaceae

Submerged perennial aquatics, with whorled leaves split into narrow lobes. Solitary, inconspicuous male and female flowers are borne in the leaf nodes on separate plants.

Rigid hornwort

Ceratophyllum demersum

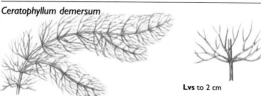

Lvs to 2 cm

Stiff waterweed, some stems to 1 m long. Lvs serrate, divided once or twice. Fr oval, to 4 mm, 2 spines at base but hard to see. *D:* T; *Fl:* 7–9

Buttercup family Ranunculaceae

Herbs, woody plants and climbers, often poisonous and usually with spirally arranged leaves without stipules. The flowers vary widely but have many stamens and tend to attract insects.

Meadow buttercup

Ranunculus acris

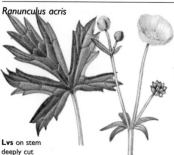

Lvs on stem deeply cut

Erect per; stem branched, hry. Basal lvs not cut. Fls to 2.5 cm on hry, unridged stks. Spls hairy, uprt. *Ht:* to 1 m; *D:* T; *Fl:* 6–7

Goldilocks buttercup

R. auricomus

Hairy per; upper leaves 3-lobed. Up to 5 ptls of uneven size. *Ht:* 30 cm; *D:* T; *Fl:* 4–5

Large white buttercup

R. platanifolius

Tall per to 1.3 m, hry below. Lvs have 5–7 palmate lobes, not deeply cut. Fls to 2 cm, ptls small, fl stks 4–5 × lf length. *D:* C, S; *Fl:* 5–8

Celery-leaved buttercup

R. sceleratus

Robust ann; stems hollow, furrowed. Ptls small. To 100 or more frs per head. *Ht:* 45 cm; *D:* T; *Fl:* 7–9

Corn buttercup

R. arvensis

Branched; upper lvs 3-lobed. Fl stks hry, fr spined. *Ht:* 80 cm; *D:* S, W, C; *Fl:* 6–7

Bulbous buttercup

R. bulbosus

Bulbous swelling at sh base. Spls bent back, hry below. *Ht:* 35 cm; *D:* T; *Fl:* 5–6

Glacial buttercup

R. glacialis

Perennial; lvs and stem hrlss. Lvs fleshy, 3-lobed. Fls sol; spls hry, uprt. *Ht:* 15 cm; *D:* N, C; *Fl:* 6–8

Lesser celandine

R. ficaria

Has many rt tubers and may be bulbils in axils. Fls sol, 8–12 ptls. *Ht:* 20 cm; *D:* T; *Fl:* 3–5

Lesser spearwort

R. flammula

Lower stems have rts. Upper stems hollow, hrlss above. Basal lvs spear-shaped. *Ht:* 50 cm; *D:* T; *Fl:* 6–8

Greater spearwort

R. lingua

Branched per. Uprt, near-hrlss, hollow stems to 1.2 m rise from creeping base. Stem lvs unstkd. Fl 4 cm. *D:* T; *Fl:* 6–9

Creeping buttercup

R. repens

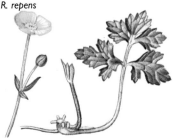

Erect per to 60 cm. Creeping runners root at nodes. Basal lvs 3-lobed, middle lobe stkd. Fl stks ridged, hry. Spls uprt or spread. *D:* T; *Fl:* 5–8

Water crowfoot		Ivy-leaved crowfoot	

Ranunculus aquatilis

Floating lvs
lobed

R. hederaceus

Fl to 6 mm.
6–10 stms

Branched, hrlss; fine-cut submerged lvs in many planes. Fls 3 cm, 15 or more long stamens. *D:* T; *Fl:* 5–8

Branched per. Creeping stems to 40 cm. Lvs opp, stkd, 3–5 lobed. No submerged lvs. *D:* T; *Fl:* 6–9

River water crowfoot

R. fluitans

Fls to 3 cm, many
short stamens

Robust waterweed with deeply divided, submerged lvs to 30 cm with a few long segments. Stems to 6 m. Usually no floating lvs. *D:* W, C; *Fl:* 6–8

Hairy buttercup

R. sardous

Similar to *R. bulbosus* (p. 29), but annual and stems without swollen base. Hairy leaves; sepals bent back. Fr with small warts. *Ht:* 10–40 cm; *D:* T (except N); *Fl:* 6–10

Wood anemone		Yellow anemone	

Anemone nemorosa

Fls have 6–7
ptls, no spls

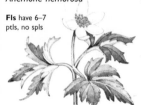

A. ranunculoides

Perennial; lvs borne on creeping rhizome and fl stems. Fls to 4 cm, sol. *Ht:* 20 cm; *D:* T; *Fl:* 3–5

Stem lvs on v short stks. One or more fls per fl stk. Fls 2 cm diam;. 5 ptls. *Ht:* 20 cm; *D:* T; *Fl:* 3–5

Narcissus-flowered anemone

A. narcissiflora

Robust and hry. Basal leaves long-stkd, stem leaves unstkd. Fls to 3 cm on 4 cm stks. *Ht*: 30 cm; *D*: T; *Fl*: 6–7

Snowdrop windflower

A. sylvestris

   Fl to 7 cm

Hairy, has rt buds. Basal lvs long-stalked, lobed, fl sol. *Ht*: 35 cm; *D*: C, E; *Fl*: 2–6

Forking larkspur

Consolida regalis

 **Fl** long-spurred

Annual; brs spread, hry. Few fls in infl, fr single, hrlss. *Ht*: 40 cm; *D*: S, W, C, E; *Fl*: 6–7

Marsh marigold

Caltha palustris

Hairless; lvs round or kidney-shaped, fine teeth, no true ptls. *Ht*: 20 cm; *D*: T; *Fl*: 3–7

Alpine larkspur

Delphinium elatum

Stem hrlss above. Upper lvs short-stkd; 3 hrlss frs per fl. *Ht*: to 2 m; *D*: C, S; *Fl*: 6–8

Columbine

Aquilega vulgaris

Leaves long-stkd, hrlss. Lflts stkd. Spurs knobbed. *Ht*: 70 cm; *D*: W, C; *Fl*: 3–6

Monkshood

Aconitum napellus

Leaves deeply lobed. Wide hoods on fls; 3 frs per fl. *Ht*: 70 cm; *D*: W, C; *Fl*: 5–6

31

Globe flower

Trollius europaeus

Pasque flower

Pulsatilla vulgaris

Erect, hrlss per. Basal lvs stkd, stem lvs unstkd. Fls consist of spls and nectaries. *Ht:* 40 cm; *D:* T (not far N); *Fl:* 6–8

Has rosette of long-stkd, hry, v cut lvs. Fls sol, 8 cm, ptls hry to 3 × stamen length. *Ht:* 20 cm; *D:* NW; *Fl:* 4–5

Small pasque flower

P. pratensis

Pale pasque flower

P. vernalis

Small per to 10 cm, but to 45 cm in fr. Lvs hry, v cut. Fls to 4 cm, ptls under 1.5 × stamen length. *D:* C, E; *Fl:* 5

Perennial to 15 cm, but to 35 cm in fr. Basal lvs evergreen. Fls to 6 cm nodding at first, then erect. *D:* C, N; *Fl:* 4–6

Winter aconite

Eranthis hyemalis

Hairless per. Lvs palmately 3–5-lobed, arise after fls. 6 spls, ptl-like, 30 stamens, 6 carpels, fls to 3 cm. *Ht:* 10 cm; *D:* C, S, W; *Fl:* 1–3

Helleborus foetidus

Strong-smelling per to 80 cm. Basal lvs evergreen;, topmost lvs small, undivided. Fls 3 cm, many per sh, never wide open. *D:* S, W; *Fl:* 3–4

Summer pheasant's eye

Adonis aestivalis

Erect ann; lvs v cut. Fls 2 cm, 5 spls cling to spread ptls. *Ht:* 25 cm; *D:* T (not N); *Fl:* 6–8

Green hellebore

Helleborus viridis

Erect per to 40 cm. Lvs long-stkd, hrlss, serrate, palmately divided. Fls to 5 cm, wide-spread ptls and 3 carpels. *D:* W, C; *Fl:* 3–4

Pheasant's eye

A. annua

Upright ann. Lvs hrlss, v cut. Fls to 2 cm, spls do not touch ptls. *Ht:* 25 cm; *D:* S; *Fl:* 6–8

Yellow pheasant's eye

A. vernalis

Erect per to 40 cm, base scaly. Stem lvs unstkd, cut twice. Ptls 2 × spl length. *D:* E, S, C; *Fl:* 4–5

33

Peony

Paeonia officinalis

Woody, stemmed perennial. Lower lvs hrlss above, cut into 17–30 segments. Fls to 1.3 cm, fr has 2–3 hry follicles. *Ht:* 50 cm; *D:* S; *Fl:* 5–6

Hepatica

Hepatica nobilis

Lvs and fls arise direct from short stock; lvs 3-lobed, purplish below. Fls 2 cm, 3 bracts. *Ht:* 10 cm; *D:* T (not far N); *Fl:* 3–5

Common meadow rue

Baneberry

Actaea spicata

Strong-smelling. Lvs pinnate. Infl dense, long stamens; fruit a berry. *Ht:* 40 cm; *D:* T; *Fl:* 5–6

Lesser meadow rue

Thalictrum minus

T. flavum

Alpine meadow rue

T. alpinum

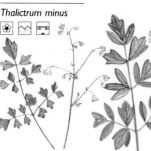

Tufted perennial. Lvs pinnate, 3–4 × divided, lflts as broad as long. Infl loose, drooping stamens, fr uprt. *Ht:* 85 cm; *D:* T; *Fl:* 6–8

Leaves 2–3 × cut, lower stkd; lflts longer than broad. Infl dense, stms erect. *Ht:* 75 cm; *D:* T; *Fl:* 7–8

Slender per to 15 cm. Lvs 2 × cut, mostly arise from a rhizome. Stamens hanging, yellow and purple stks. *D:* N, C; *Fl:* 6–7

Mousetail

Myosurus minimus

Traveller's joy

Clematis vitalba

Hairless ann. Narrow, undivided lvs in basal rosette. Fls small, in a spike, 5–10 stamens. *Ht:* 9 cm; *D:* T; *Fl:* 6–7

Woody climbing per, stems to 30 m. Lvs have 5 coarsely toothed lflts. Fls to 2 cm, 4 hry ptls; long feathery styles on fr. *D:* T (not N); *Fl:* 7–8

Poppy family Papaveraceae

Herbs with deeply divided leaves. True poppies have a milky juice in all parts but the fumitories (now part of the family) do not. The flowers have 4 petals and two or many stamens.

Common poppy

Papaver rhoeas

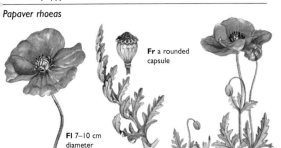

Fr a rounded capsule

Fl 7–10 cm diameter

Erect, branching annual to 60 cm. Stems covered in spreading, bristly hrs. Lvs compound, pinnately divided, large central lobe. *D:* T; *Fl:* 6–8

Arctic poppy

P. radicatum

Long-headed poppy

P. dubium

Prickly poppy

P. argemone

Tufted per, juice yellow. Lf bases persist assheaths. Fls to 5 cm, fr a bristly elliptic-ovoid capsule. *Ht:* 15 cm; *D:* NW; *Fl:* 7

Erect branched ann, flat hrs above. Fr to ∠.5 cm, 2 × as long as wide. *Ht:* 40 cm; *D:* T; *Fl:* 6–7

Upright ann to 45 cm, flat hrs on stems. Lf tips v pointed. Fls to 6 cm; fr ridged, bristly, to 2.5 cm. *D:* S; *Fl:* 6–7

Welsh poppy

Meconopsis cambrica

Yellow horned-poppy

Glaucium flavum

Tufted, hrlss stems to 60 cm. Basal lvs long-stkd. Fls to 8 cm, 2 hry spls; 4 ptls; fr oval, 4–6 valves. *D:* W; *Fl:* 6–8

Branched, glaucous, to 90 cm, basal lvs hry. Fls short-stkd, fr to 30 cm. *D:* W; *Fl:* 6–9

Greater celandine	Bulbous corydalis

Chelidonium majus   *Corydalis solida*

Erect to 20 cm. Lobed bracts below fls. *D:* T (not far N); *Fl:* 4–5. *C. bulbosa* similar but bracts unlobed.

Stems fragile, to 90 cm, scattered hrs. Orange sap. Fls to 2 cm, fr to 5 cm. *D:* T; *Fl:* 5–8

Climbing corydalis	Yellow corydalis	Common fumitory

Ceratocapnos claviculata   *Pseudofumaria lutea*   *Fumaria officinalis*

Infl of 6–10 fls

Scrambling; lvs end in tendril. Ptl tube short-spurred, 6 fls in infl. *Ht:* 50 cm; *D:* W; *Fl:* 6–9

Branched, no tendrils. Ptl tube short-spurred to 1.8 cm. *Ht:* to 30 cm; *D:* W, C; *Fl:* 5–8

Scrambling, hrlss. Lvs cut 2 × into linear lobes. Ptl tube 8 mm, 2 spls, 10–40 fls per infl. Fr a nutlet. *Ht:* 10 cm; *D:* T; *Fl:* 5–10

Cabbage family Brassicaceae

Annuals and perennials with spirally arranged leaves. The flowers have 4 sepals, 4 unjoined petals, 6 stamens and 1 stigma. The fruit opens by two valves. Many are weeds.

Wallflower

Cheiranthus cheiri

Erect, branched perennial to 60 cm. Stems woody and ridged. Basal lvs 5–10 cm long, undivided and covered with forked hairs. Fls to 2.5 cm diam, ptls sepal length × 2. Fruit 3–7 cm long. *D:* W, S, C; *Fl:* 4–6

Shepherd's purse

Capsella bursa-pastoris

Fls c. 2.5 mm

Stem lvs clasping, with pointed lobes. Ptls 2 × spl length, fr 9 mm. *Ht:* 25 cm; *D:* T; *Fl:* 1–12

Hairy rocket

Erucastrum gallicum

Fr to 4 cm, curved

Erect ann to 60 cm, hrs point down. Lobed lvs, bracts at infl base. Fls 8 mm, slender beak on fr. *D:* SW, C; *Fl:* 5–9

Annual wall rocket

Diplotaxis muralis

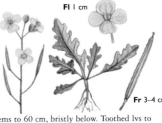

Fl 1 cm

Fr 3–4 cm

Stems to 60 cm, bristly below. Toothed lvs to 10 cm. Strong-smelling. Ptls 2 × spl length. *D:* S, C; *Fl:* 6–9

Small Alison

Alyssum alyssoides

Lvs less than 2 cm

Fr to 4 mm

Erect ann, star-shaped hrs on shs. Fls 3 mm, spls persist in fr. *Ht:* 15 cm; *D:* T; *Fl:* 5–6

London rocket

Sisymbrium irio

Fr to 5 cm

Lower lvs stkd, lobed; stem lvs stkd. No bracts. Fls 4 mm. *Ht:* 40 cm; *D:* T (not far N); *Fl:* 6–8

Hedge mustard

Sisymbrium officinale

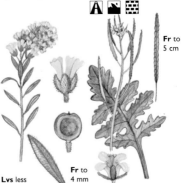

Fl 3 mm

Stiffly erect ann to 90 cm. Downward-pointing hrs on stems; basal lvs in rosette, deeply lobed, no bracts. Fr narrow, erect. *D:* T; *Fl:* 6–8

37

Field pepperwort	Dittander	Fixweed

Lepidium campestre

L. latifolium

Descurainia sophia

Upper lvs clasp stem

Has short, spreading hrs. Lvs unlobed. Fr notched at tip, spotted white. *Ht:* 40 cm: *D:* T; *Fl:* 5–8

Branched, hrlss; basal lvs serrate. Spls white-edged, fr unnotched. *Ht:* 1 m; *D:* T (not N); *Fl:* 6–7

Lvs v divided

Erect with star-shaped hrs. Fls 3 mm, fr 2 cm, strong midrib. *Ht:* 60 cm; *D:* T; *Fl:* 6–8

Sea kale

Crambe maritima

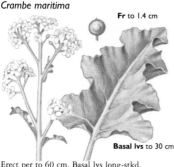

Fr to 1.4 cm

Basal lvs to 30 cm

Erect per to 60 cm. Basal lvs long-stkd, glaucous. Ptls have green claws, fr 1-seeded. *D:* T; *Fl:* 6–8

Sea rocket

Cakile maritima

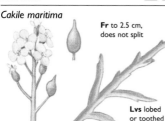

Fr to 2.5 cm, does not split

Lvs lobed or toothed

Often prostrate succ to 45 cm. Infl dense, fr in 2 sections, 1 seed in each. *D:* T (not far N); *Fl:* 6–8

Sea stock

Matthiola sinuata

Stem lvs elliptical

Branched hrs on stems, sticky hrs on stem lvs. Basal lvs wavy. Fls *c.* 2.5 cm, fr 10 cm. *Ht:* 40 cm; *D:* W, S; *Fl:* 6–8

Hoary whitlow grass

Draba incana

Fr to 9 mm, twisted, elliptical

Basal lvs serrate with star-shaped hrs. Fls 5 mm, ptls just notched. *Ht:* 30 cm; *D:* N, mts in C, W; *Fl:* 6–8

Yellow whitlow grass

D. aizoides

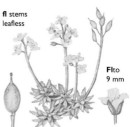

fl stems leafless

Fl to 9 mm

Hairless per. Tufted rosette of stiff, linear lvs, keeled, white spine at tip. Fr 1 cm. *Ht:* 7 cm; *D:* C, S; *Fl:* 3–5

Alpine whitlow grass

D. alpina

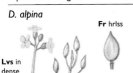

Fr hrlss

Lvs in dense rosettes

Ptls to 5 mm

Represents complex group of spp. All have star-shaped hrs on leaves. *Ht:* 15 cm; *D:* Arct *Fl:* 7–8

Common whitlow grass

Erophila verna

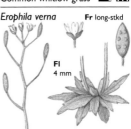

Fr long-stkd

Fl 4 mm

Variable low, hry ann. Lvs in basal rosette. Ptls v deeply cut, fr elliptical, hrlss. *Ht:* to 20 cm; *D:* T, *Fl:* 3–5

Common scurvy grass

Cochlearia officinalis

Basal lvs long-stkd, upper lvs clasping. Fr 5 mm. *Ht:* 35 cm; *D:* NW; *Fl:* 5–8

English scurvy grass

C. anglica

Basal lvs taper to stk. Fls to 1.4 cm, fr oval, flattened, 1 cm. *Ht:* 25 cm; *D:* NW; *Fl:* 4–7

Alpine scurvy grass

C. pyrenaica

Very like *C. officinalis* and possibly the same sp as *C. alpina*. Lvs not succ. Fr tapers into stk and tip. *Ht:* 25 cm; *D:* C, W; *Fl:* 5–8

Early scurvy grass | Tower cress

Cochlearia danica | Arabis turrita

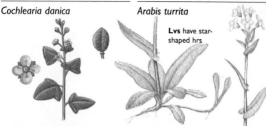

Lvs have star-shaped hrs

Like *C. officinalis* but with upper lvs stkd and fls smaller (less than 5 mm). Lvs 3–7 lobed. *Ht:* 5–20 cm; *D:* W and N; *Fl:* 1–6

Biennial or per, horizontal at base with veg rosettes. Hry erect fl shs to 70 cm. Basal lvs serrate, narrow to stk, stem lvs oblong. *D:* C, S; *Fl:* 5–8

Hairy rock cress | Alpine rock cress | Great yellowcress

A. hirsuta | A. alpina | Rorippa amphibia

Stems to 60 cm from rosette of obovate stkd lvs, hrs star-shaped; fr 4 cm. *D:* T; *Fl:* 6–8

Creeping, erect fl shs to 40 cm. Basal lvs serrate, stkd. Fr 4 cm, spreading. *D:* N, W, S; *Fl:* 6–8

Hollow hrlss stems to 1.2 m. Ptls 2 × length of spls, fr long-stkd. *D:* T (not far N); *Fl:* 6–8

Marsh yellowcress | Thale cress | Swine cress

R. islandica | Arabidopsis thaliana | Coronopus squamatus

Fr 3 mm

Ridged stems to 60 cm. Lower lvs stkd, v cut. Ptls equal spls in length, fr curved. *D:* T; *Fl:* 6–9

Erect shs to 50 cm, hry below; stem lvs unstkd. Fr 1.5 cm, erect on spread stks. *D:* T (not far N): *Fl:* 4–5 (and 9–10)

Prostrate lfy shs 20 cm. Lvs pinnately lobed. Infl unstkd, mostly opp lvs; fr short-stkd. *D:* W, C, S; *Fl:* 6–9

Watercress

Rorippa nasturtium-aquaticum

Lvs pinnate

Hollow hrlss shs creep and float. Fr has 2 rows of seeds. *Ht:* 40 cm; *D:* T (not N); *Fl:* 5–10

Common wintercress

Barbarea vulgaris

Erect, hrlss, branched to 90 cm. Basal lvs stkd in rosette. Fr erect, and 4-angled. *D:* T; *Fl:* 5–8

Cuckoo flower

Cardamine pratense

Erect per to 60 cm. Top lflt kidney-shaped. Fls long-stkd, ptls 3 × spl length, valves of fr curl up. *D:* T; *Fl:* 4–6

Coralroot bittercress

C. bulbifera

Has bulbils in stem lf axils. Shs to 70 cm. Ptls 1.5 cm, 3 × spl length. *D:* T (not far N); *Fl:* 4–6

Wavy bittercress

C. flexuosa

Lvs pinnate, basal lvs stkd

Stems to 50 cm, may be hry; ptls same length as spls, 6 stamens. Fr hardly extends above fls. *D:* W; *Fl:* 4–9

Hairy bittercress

C. hirsuta

Stems hrlss. Fls have 4 stamens; fr grows above fls. *Ht:* 20 cm; *D:* T (not far N); *Fl:* 4–7

Large bittercress

C. amara

Lower lvs pinnately stkd

Creeping; erect shs to 60 cm. Fr 3 cm, long persistent style. D: T (not far N); *Fl:* 4–6

41

Field pennycress

Thlaspi arvense

Fr to 2.2 cm, tip notched

Erect, stems to 60 cm. Basal lvs broad, taper to stk. Fls 5 mm, fr broad-winged. *D:* T; *Fl:* 5–7

Hoary cress

Cardaria draba

Creeping; uprt lfy shs to 90 cm. Basal lvs stkd, upper lvs clasping. Fr does not split. *D:* T; *Fl:* 5–6

Horse radish

Armoracia rusticana

Wild radish

Raphanus raphanistrum

Bristly, basal lvs have large top lobe. Ptls veined. Long-beaked fr splits crosswise. *Ht:* 40 cm; *D:* T; *Fl:* 5–9

Robust, hrlss. Rts fleshy, edible. Basal lvs 40 cm, wavy-edged. Infl v branched. *Ht:* 1 m; *D:* T; *Fl:* 5–6

Sea radish

R. maritimus

Bristly hrs above. Ptls *c.* 2 cm, not veined. Fr short-beaked, does not split. *D:* W, N to GB; *Fl:* 6–8

Charlock

Sinapis arvensis

Fr 3 cm, veined, bristly

Stems to 80 cm with bristly hrs. Basal lvs lobed, upper lvs serrate, unlobed. Fr smooth. *D:* T; *Fl:* 5–7

White mustard

S. alba

Like *S. arvensis* (p. 42) but all lvs pinnately lobed. Fr beaked. *Ht:* 60 cm; *D:* T; *Fl:* 6–8

Wild cabbage

Brassica oleracea

Fr 5–10 cm, short beak

Thick rootstock, stem has lf scars. Lower lvs large, few basal lobes; upper lvs stkd, oblong. Ptls 2 cm. *Ht:* to 3 m; *D:* W, N to GB; *Fl:* 5–8

Black mustard

Brassica nigra

Annual to 1 m, bristly below. No thick rootstock, all lvs stkd. Ridged fr held near stem. *D:* T; *Fl:* 6–9

Garlic mustard

Alliaria petiolata

Roots and lvs smell of garlic. Stem hry. Fr 4-angled. *Ht:* 1 m; *D:* T (not far N); *Fl:* 4–6

Treacle mustard

Erysimum cheiranthoides

Leafy stem to 90 cm, hrs branched. Basal leaves die when infl formed; fr 4-angled. *D:* T; *Fl:* 6–8

Perennial wall-rocket

Diplotaxis tenuifolia

Stems hairless and lvs bluish-green, deeply and narrowly lobed. Fr often shorter than its stalk. *Ht:* 30–80 cm; *D:* C, S; *Fl:* 5–9

Lesser swinecress

Coronopus didymus

Prostrate stems to 40 cm often hry, strong-smelling. Lvs narrowly lobed. Fr stks longer than fr. 2 stamens. *D:* T; *Fl:* 7–9

Perennial honesty	Woad
Lunaria rediviva	*Isatis tinctoria*

Fr to 2 cm

Plant used as dye

Erect to 1.4 m. Top lvs stkd (unlike *L. annua*). Infl at apex, fr oval. *D:* T (not far N); *Fl:* 4–6

Hairless, several basal rosettes, stem lvs arrow-shaped, hanging fr. *Ht:* 1·m; *D:* T (not N); *Fl:* 7–8

Mignonette family Resedaceae

Herbs with simple or divided, leaves spirally arranged. Flowers have 4–7 unfused petals and sepals, many stamens and 3–6 carpels fusing into a 1-celled capsule.

Wild mignonette	Upright mignonette
Reseda lutea	*R. alba*

Fr to 1.8 cm, 3 lobes at tip

Branched, erect, hrlss to 75 cm. Basal lvs in rosette, pinnate stem lvs. Fls 6 mm, 6 ptls and spls, fr erect. *D:* S, W, C; *Fl:* 6–8

Leaves deeply cut into narrow pinnate lobes. Fls 9 mm, 5 ptls, fr oblong, 4 lobes at tip. *Ht:* 75 cm; *D:* S, C, NW; *Fl:* 6–8

| Rampion mignonette | | Weld | |

R. phyteuma

R. luteola

Fr to 1.4 cm

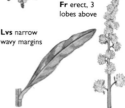

Fr erect, 3 lobes above

Lvs narrow wavy margins

Branched to 30 cm. Lvs unlobed or in prs, blunt lobes above, 6 ptls, fr drooping, 3-lobed. *D*: S; *Fl*: 6–8

Erect, hrlss to 1.5 m, little- or not branched. Lf rosette in 1st yr, fl sh in 2nd. *D*: S, W, C; *Fl*: 6–8

Sundew family Droseraceae

Perennial herbs. The leaves have sticky hairs for trapping insects and are curled in bud. Flowers have 4–8 petals.

| Common sundew | |

Drosera rotundifolia

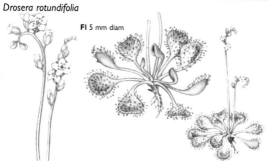

Fl 5 mm diam

Perennial with low rosettes of leaves, each 1 cm across with a long hry stk and circular blade. Erect fl shs to 25 cm and more than 2 × lf length from rosette centre. Fr pointed. *D*: T; *Fl*: 6–8

| Great sundew | | Oblong-leaved sundew | |

D. longifolia

D. intermedia

Lf blades to 3 cm

Lf stk hrlss

Erect lvs narrow to hrlss stks. Fl sh 2 × lf length from rosette centre; fr round. *D*: N, C; *Fl*: 7–8

Oblong lvs C. 10 cm just shorter than fl sh arising under rosette, fr pointed. *D*: N, W, C; *Fl*: 7–8

Stonecrop family Crassulaceae

Usually succulent herbs with undivided leaves. The flowers generally have 5 sepals and petals, but there may be more than this. The stamens are equal to or double the petals in number and there are as many unjoined carpels as petals.

Biting stonecrop

Sedum acre

Fl 1.2 cm

Creeping evergreen to 10 cm. Sometimes confused with *S. anglicum* but flowers are bright yellow. Shs erect, hrlss; lvs unstkd, 5 ptls and pointed spls. *D:* T; *Fl:* 6–7

White stonecrop

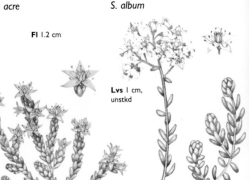

S. album

Lvs 1 cm, unstkd

Carpet-forming evergreen to 15 cm. Infl much-branched, flat-topped, fl 9 mm. *D:* T (not NE); *Fl:* 6–8

Rock stonecrop

S. forsteranum

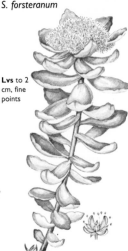

Lvs to 2 cm, fine points

Fl 1.2 cm, 6–8 ptls

Creeping, glaucous. Old lvs stay on stems, new ones arise at tips. *Ht:* 22 cm; *D:* W; *Fl:* 6–7

English stonecrop

S. anglicum

Patch-forming, hrlss. Stems short and slightly branched. Lvs globular, alternate. Fl short. *Ht:* 4 cm; *D:* W, N to Swed; *Fl:* 6–9

S. rosea

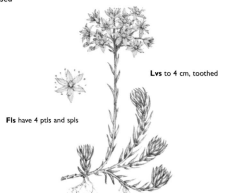

Lvs to 4 cm, toothed

Fls have 4 ptls and spls

Robust, erect, glaucous per; short stock bears lf scars. Lvs flat, round. ♂ and ♀ separate. *Ht:* 22 cm; *D:* N, mts in C; *Fl:* 5–8

Navelwort

Umbilicus rupestris

Hairless, usually unbranched. Lf blade circular, central stk; fl tubular. *Ht:* 30 cm; *D:* S, W; *Fl:* 6–8

Mossy stonecrop

Crassula tillaea

Dwarf, hrlss. Shs creeping, often reddish. Lvs and fls dense, 3 ptls and spls. *Ht:* 4 cm; *D:* S, W; *Fl:* 6–7

Reflexed stonecrop

S. rupestre

Fl 1.4 cm, 7 ptls and spls

Lvs not flat

More robust than *S. forsterianum*. Top lvs bent back at tip, dead lvs fall off. *Ht:* 25 cm; *D:* T; *Fl:* 6–8. *S. telephium* (orpine) similar but pink fls.

Saxifrage family Saxifragaceae

Herbs with alternate leaves. The symmetrical flowers usually have 5 petals and sepals, either 5 or 10 stamens and two carpels which are joined at their base.

Meadow saxifrage

Saxifraga granulata

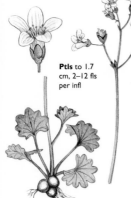

Ptls to 1.7 cm, 2–12 fls per infl

Rosette of *c.* 7 lvs, some long hrs; bulbils in lf axils. Fls have 10 stamens as all *Saxifraga* spp. *Ht:* 35 cm; *D:* N, C; *Fl:* 4–6

Mossy saxifrage

S. hypnoides

Mat-forming. Lvs 3–5-lobed with sharp points, narrow to stk; stem hrlss. Fl shs fine to 20 cm, ptls to 1 cm. *D:* NW; *Fl:* 5–7

Rue-leaved saxifrage

S. tridactylites

Upright to 15 cm, sticky hrs all over. Lvs 3–5 lobed, dense at base. Fls sol or in gps on long stks, ptls to 3 mm long. *D:* T (not far N); *Fl:* 4–6

Arctic saxifrage

S. nivalis

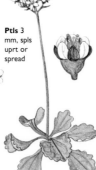

Ptls 3 mm, spls uprt or spread

Leaves to 2 cm, oval or spathulate, serrate, purple below in basal rosette. Infl dense, 3–12 fls, fl sh to 15 cm. *D:* N; *Fl:* 7–8

Drooping saxifrage

S. cernua

Ptls 1.3 cm

Basal lvs 3–5 lobed in rosette, top lvs unstkd, bulbils in axils. Fl shs unbranched, fl sol on bulbil gp. *Ht:* 10 cm; *D:* N, Alps; *Fl:* 7

Purple saxifrage

S. oppositifolia

Ptls to 1 cm

Perennial with long, prostrate branches. Erect shs only 1–2 cm tall. Dense lvs in 4 ranks. Fls sol on erect shs. *D:* N, S; *Fl:* 3–5

Yellow saxifrage

S. aizoides

Starry saxifrage

S. stellaris

Perennial. Vegetative and flowering shs to 20 cm tall. Lvs linear, unstkd, dense. Fl shs hry, infl of 1–10 fls with lfy bracts, spls spread, ptls to 7 mm long. *D:* N, mts in S; *Fl:* 6–9

Basal lvs as *S. nivalis* (p. 48) but green, few long hrs. Over 12 fls in infl, spls reflexed. *Ht:* 10 cm; *D:* T; *Fl:* 6–8

Opposite-leaved golden saxifrage

Chrysosplenium oppositifolium

Alternate-leaved golden saxifrage

C. alternifolium

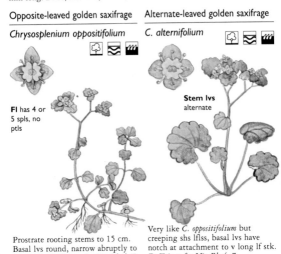

Fl has 4 or 5 spls, no ptls

Stem lvs alternate

Prostrate rooting stems to 15 cm. Basal lvs round, narrow abruptly to short stk. *D:* T (not far N); *Fl:* 4–7

Very like *C. oppositifolium* but creeping shs lflss, basal lvs have notch at attachment to v long lf stk. *D:* T (not far N); *Fl:* 4–7

49

Grass of Parnassus family Saxifragaceae

Perennial herbs with undivided, alternate leaves. Terminal, solitary flowers have 5 sepals and petals, 5 true stamens plus 5 infertile structures and 4 fused carpels.

Grass of Parnassus

Parnassia palustris

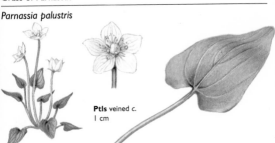

Ptls veined *c.* 1 cm

Hairless herb to 30 cm. Lvs heart-shaped, untoothed to 3 cm, stks longer than blades. Fl stks vertical, single lf near base. *D*: T; *Fl*: 7–10

Rose family Rosaceae

Herbs, shrubs and trees with alternate leaves having stipules. The flowers have 5 petals and sepals (and sometimes an epicalyx), more than 5 stamens and from one to many carpels. The flower stalk is often involved in fruit formation.

Dog rose | Field rose

Rosa canina | *R. arvensis*

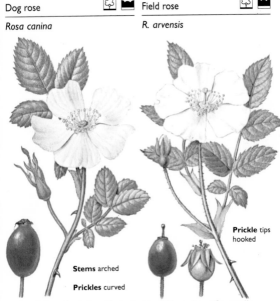

Stems arched

Prickles curved

Prickle tips hooked

Leaflets hrlss or hry below. Fl stks 1 cm, spls fall before fr ripe, stigmas unfused, fr hrlss. *Ht*: 2.5 m; *D*: T (not far N); *Fl*: 6–7

Scrambles to 2 m. Lflts usually hrlss. Fl shs to 4 cm, short spls soon fall, single style as long as stamens. *D*: C, S, W; *Fl*: 6–7

Burnet rose

R. pimpinellifolia

Fr dark

Bush to 1 m. Straight prickles and stiff hrs on stems; 3–5 lflt prs. *D:* T (not Scand); *Fl:* 5–7

Downy rose

R. tomentosa

Prickles just curved; lvs have downy hrs; fl shs sticky, hry; spls fall. *Ht:* 1.5 m; *D:* T (not far N); *Fl:* 6–7

Sweet briar

R. rubiginosa

Stems uprt, hooked prickles vary in size; lflts have glands below. *Ht:* 1.5 m;. *D:* T (not far N); *Fl:* 6–7

Wild rose

R. stylosa

Fl to 3 mm

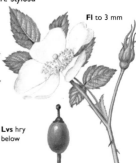

Lvs hry below

Arched shs 3 m, prickles hooked. Sticky hrs on fl shs; styles fused, separate in fr. *D:* W, S; *Fl:* 6–7

Pirri-pirri-bur

Acaena novae-zelandiae

Mat-forming woody stems with 7–9-lobed pinnate lvs, glossy green above. Spherical infl giving spiny-hooked, ball-like fr. *Ht:* 2–15 cm; *D:* W; *Fl:* 6–7

Creeping cinquefoil

Potentilla reptans

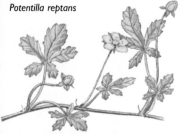

Prostrate, rts at nodes. Erect fl shs to 30 cm. Stipules untoothed. Fl has epicalyx as in all spp of *Potentilla*. *D:* T (not far N); *Fl:* 6–9

Silverweed

P. anserina

Creeping stolons to 1 m; 10 lflt prs, silky white hrs. Fls long-stkd, sol. *D:* T; *Fl:* 6–8

Shrubby cinquefoil

P. fruticosa

Ptls to 1.2 cm

Lvs untoothed

Shrub; lvs pinnate, 5-lobed. Fls in terminal infl. *Ht:* to 1 m; *D:* NW, mts in S; *Fl:* 6–7

Hoary cinquefoil

P. argentea

Lower lvs 5-lobed, v hry below

Upright fl shs often hry. Fls to 1.5 cm, spls hry. *Ht:* 40 cm; *D:* N, Alps; *Fl:* 6–9

Tormentil

P. erecta

Prostrate shs from lf rosette. Fls 1 cm, only 4 spls and ptls. *Ht:* 40 cm; *D:* T; *Fl:* 6–9

Barren strawberry

P. sterilis
Fl to 1.5 cm

Softly hry to 15 cm, spread stolons, lvs not glossy, ptls far apart. *D:* W, S, C; *Fl:* 2–5

Marsh cinquefoil

P. palustris

Spls pointed

Has creeping rhizome. Lvs serrate, 5 or 7 lflts, spls purple. *Ht:* 35 cm; *D:* T; *Fl:* 5–7

Norwegian cinquefoil

P. norvegica

Leaves serrate, hry; fl shs erect, clustered fls, 5 hry spls. *Ht:* 40 cm; *D:* N, C, E; *Fl:* 6–9

Alpine cinquefoil

P. crantzii

Fl large, to 2.5 cm

Lower lvs 5-lobed, hry, especially below; fl shs in lf axils, spls hry. *Ht:* 20 cm; *D:* N, S; *Fl:* 6–7

Wild strawberry

Fragaria vesca

Fl stks have flat hrs above

Lvs glossy above

Like *P. sterilis* (p. 52) but no gaps between ptls; achenes all over fr. *Ht:* 20 cm; *D:* T; *Fl:* 4–7

Sibbaldia

Sibbaldia procumbens

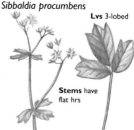

Lvs 3-lobed

Stems have flat hrs

Tussocky. Infl dense, fls 5 mm, spls pointed, ptls v small or absent. *Ht:* 2 cm; *D:* N, S; *Fl:* 7–8

Cloudberry

Rubus chamaemorus

Uprt spineless stems, 5–7 lobes on lvs. Fls sol terminal. *Ht:* 5–20 cm; *D:* N & C; *Fl:* 6–8

Raspberry

R. idaeus

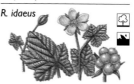

Erect suckering stems, straight prickles; 3–7-lobed lvs, white, hairy on lower side. Infl up to 10 fls in lf axils. *Ht:* 1–1.6 m; *D:* T; *Fl:* 6–8

Stone bramble

R. saxatilis

Infl dense

Fr of 2–6 parts

Prostrate, uprt fl shs 35 cm; lvs 3-lobed (unlike *R. chamaemorus*). *D:* T; *Fl:* 6–8

Arctic bramble

R. arcticus

Fl has 5–7 ptls

No prickles; 3-lobed lvs, infl long-stkd, 1–3 fls, many fr parts. *Ht:* 20 cm; *D:* N; *Fl:* 7–9

Bramble

R. fruticosus

Curved prickles; fr of 20+ parts, no bloom (unlike *R. caesius*). *Ht:* 1.5 m; *D:* T; *Fl:* 5–9

Water avens	Herb bennet

Geum rivale

G. urbanum

Basal lvs pinnate

Hairy; top lflt large. Fls nodding, spls purple, styles persist in fr. *Ht:* 45 cm; *D:* T; *Fl:* 5–9

Stem lvs simple above, lobed lower down. Fls uprt, spls green. *Ht:* 45 cm; *D:* T (not far N); *Fl:* 6–8

Mountain avens

Dryas octopetala

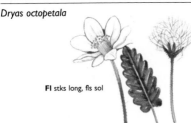

Fl stks long, fls sol

Many v hry lvs; 7–10 ptls, sticky black hrs on spls, feathery fr. *Ht:* 6 cm; *D:* S mts, N; *Fl:* 6–7

Lady's mantle	Alpine lady's mantle	Agrimony

Alchemilla vulgaris

A. alpina

Agrimonia eupatoria

Infl at spike

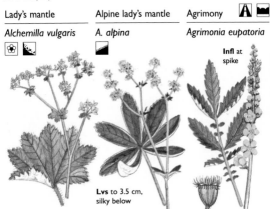

Lvs to 3.5 cm, silky below

Large lvs, lobes half radius, green below; no ptls. *Ht:* 30 cm; *D:* W, C; *Fl:* 6–9

Creeping; lf blades cut almost to centre, fls 3 mm. *Ht:* 15 cm; *D:* N, W; *Fl:* 6–8

Hairy, hooked spines on fls persist in fr. *Ht:* 60 cm; *D:* T (not far N); *Fl:* 6–8

Meadowsweet

Filipendula ulmaria

Infl dense

Leaves pinnate, 2–5 big lflts alt with small prs; 5 ptls, fr spirally twisted. *Ht:* 1 m; *D:* T; *Fl:* 6–9

Dropwort

F. vulgaris

Basal lvs jagged, 8–20 prs large lflts between small prs; 6 ptls. *Ht:* 60 cm; *D:* T (not N); *Fl:* 5–8

Great burnet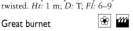

Sanguisorba officinalis

Lflts toothed

Pinnate lvs, 3–7 prs lflts; 4 red spls, no ptls, 4 stms; ♂, parts in same fl. *Ht:* 80 cm; *D:* T; *Fl:* 6–9

Parsley piert

Aphanes arvensis

Creeps to 20 cm. Lvs have 3-lobed lflts. Fls v small with only spls and stipules. *D:* W, C; *Fl:* 4–10

Salad burnet

S. minor

Basal lvs have 4–12 lflt prs

Scrambles to 60 cm; 4 green spls, no ptls, many stms; ♂ fls at top round infl, ♀ below. *D:* W, C; *Fl:* 5–8

Pea family Fabaceae

Compound leaves have stipules and possibly tendrils. Flowers have an erect (standard) petal, two wing petals and two petals joined into a keel; 5 sepals form a tube. The fruit is a pod.

Red clover

Trifolium pratense

Erect or straggling per. Lvs have 3 lflts, often with pale V mark. Stipules contracted to a fine point. Fls in dense globular heads. Forage crop. *Ht:* 30 cm; *D:* T; *Fl:* 5–9

Zig-zag clover

T. medium

Straggling per. Like *T. pratense* but lflts narrower and stipules oblong. Fl head arises from a pair of lvs. *Ht:* 30 cm; *D:* T; *Fl:* 6–9

Slender trefoil

T. micranthum

Tiny procumbent annual. Lflts only 5 mm. Infl with 1–6 fls. Standard petal deeply notched. *Ht:* 1–15 cm; *D:* W; *Fl:* 6–7

Lucerne

Medicago sativa ssp sativa

Erect perennial with pubescent lvs. Stipules linear. Fl purple. Fr a spiral pod. Planted as fodder crop. *Ht:* 20–90 cm; *D:* T; *Fl:* 6–7

White clover

T. repens

Creeping hrlss per, roots at nodes. Lflts broader near tip, white V mark, stipules oval. Spls short-toothed. *Ht:* 30 cm; *D:* T; *Fl:* 6–9

Haresfoot clover

T. arvense

Softly hry ann. Brs straggling, hry. Infl cylindrical, downy, long-stkd. Ptls half spl length. *Ht:* 10 cm; *D:* T (not far N); *Fl:* 6–9

Alsike clover

T. hybridum

Erect per. Lflts elliptic. Stipules oval, long, fine points. Teeth on spl tube 2 × tube length. Infl long-stkd. *Ht:* 40 cm; *D:* T; *Fl:* 6–9

Lesser yellow trefoil	Strawberry clover	Sulphur clover

T. dubium

Infl of up to 26 fls

Standard ptl folds round fr unlike *T. campestre* (hop trefoil). *Ht:* 15 cm; *D:* T (not far N); *Fl:* 5–10

T. fragiferum

Lflts serrated. Spls inflate round swelling head of fr. *Ht:* 20 cm; *D:* T (not far N); *Fl:* 7–9

T. ochroleucon

Hairy per; lflts to 3 cm, 2 unstkd lvs round fl head; 1 v long spl tooth. *Ht:* 30 cm; *D:* W, C, S; *Fl:* 6–7

Fenugreek

T. ornithopodioides

Delicate hrlss ann. Stipules lance-shaped. Infl has 1–3 short stkd fls. Fr curved. *Ht:* 10 cm; *D:* T; *Fl:* 5–9

Suffocated clover

T. suffocatum

Prostrate, hrlss ann. Lflts toothed, triangular, to 5 mm, stipules pointed. Infls at sh tips dense, unstkd. *Ht:* 5 cm; *D:* S, W; *Fl:* 4–8

Birdsfoot trefoil

Lotus corniculatus

Infl of 2–6 fls

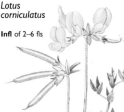

Pods twist spirally when split

Scrambling hrlss per. Stems solid. Lvs have 5 lflts. Infl horseshoe-shaped. *Ht:* 20 cm; *D:* T; *Fl:* 6–9

Marsh birdsfoot trefoil

L. pedunculatus

Erect or climbing per, sometimes hry. Stem hollow. Lflts to 2 cm. Infl with 5–12 fls on long, slim stks. *Ht:* 40 cm; *D:* W, C, S; *Fl:* 6–8

Dragon's teeth

Tetragonolobus maritimus

Like *Lotus* but lvs short-stkd, 3-lobed, big stipules; fls sol. *Ht:* 20 cm; *D:* C, S; *Fl:* 5–7

Bush vetch

V. sepium

Lflts in 5–9 prs

Trailing, hrlss to 1 m with tendrils; 2-6 fls in infl, spl teeth not equal. *D:* T; *Fl:* 5-8

Upright vetch

V. orobus

Fr to 3 cm

Has 6–9 lflt prs, no tendrils, toothed stripules; infl 6–20 fls. *Ht:* 30 cm; *D:* W; *Fl:*

Birdsfoot

Ornithopus perpusillus

Prostrate, hry; 4–13 lflt prs, lowest near stem. Infl of 3–6 fls; fruit constricted. *Ht:* 35 cm; *D:* W, C; *Fl:* 5–8

Wood vetch

V. sylvatica

Infl 6–18 fls

Scrambling, hrlss, has tendrils; 6–9 lflt prs, stipules toothed; top spl teeth short. *Ht:* 1 m; *D:* N, C, E; *Fl:* 6–8

Common vetch

Vicia sativa

Fr to 8 cm

Lflts in 4–8 prs

Scrambling with tendrils; dark spot on stipules. Fls in 1s or 2s, spl teeth equal. *Ht:* 1 m; *D:* T; *Fl:* 5–9

Tufted vetch

V. cracca

Tendrils present

Clambers to 2 m; 8–12 lflt prs; infl 10–14 fls, top spl teeth short. *D:* T; *Fl:* 6–8

Yellow vetch Hairy tare Kidney vetch

V. lutea *V. hirsuta* *Anthyllis vulneraria*

Fl to 2.5 cm

Lflts in 4–8 prs

Prostrate, hrlss; 3–7 lflt prs, triangular stipules, has tendrils; fls sol, fr hry. *Ht:* 50 cm; *D:* S, W; *Fl:* 6–8

Scrambles to 70 cm. Lflts narrow, tendrils present, stipules 4-lobed; infl 1–9 fls, fr hry. *D:* T; *Fl:* 5–8

Prostrate or uprt; lflts oval, top one v large. Infl dense, woolly spls, fls 1.5 cm. *Ht:* 50 cm; *D:* T; *Fl:* 6–9

Yellow milk vetch

Hairy milk vetch

Mountain milk vetch

Oxytropis campestris

O. pilosa

O. halleri

Hairy; 10–15 lflt prs; infl oval, 5–15 fls, keel fine-pointed as in all *Oxytropis* spp. *Ht:* 15 cm; *D:* N, S; *Fl:* 6–8

Robust, v hry per to 50 cm; 5–15 lflt prs with flat hrs. Oval infl, many fls, narrow fr with spread hrs. *D:* C, E; *Fl:* 6–8

Softly hry; 8–18 lflt prs, infl oval with 5–15 fls, keel has a long tooth *c.* 1 mm. Flat hrs on fr. *Ht:* to 30 cm; *D;* C, S; *Fl:* 6–7

59

Purple milk vetch

Astragalus danicus

Lflts in 6–13 prs

Delicate per, silky hrs. Fl sh to 2 × lf length; fr 2-celled. *Ht:* 25 cm; *D:* T; *Fl:* 5–7

Alpine milk vetch

A. alpinus

Lflts in 7–12 prs

Prostrate; lflts hrlss above. Loose infl, 5–15 fls, spls hry. *Ht:* 30 cm; *D:* N, S; *Fl:* 7–8

Yellow alpine milk vetch

A. frigidus

Lflts oval in 3–8 prs

Erect, hrlss; loose infl, 5–20 fls, teeth on spl tube triangular. *Ht:* 35 cm; *D:* N, S; *Fl:* 7–8

Wild lentil

A. cicer

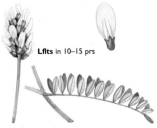

Lflts in 10–15 prs

Scrambling. Fl shs just shorter than lvs. Spl teeth half tube length. *Ht:* 65 cm; *D:* C; *Fl:* 6–7

Wild liquorice

A. glycophyllos

Plant nearly hrlss

Straggles to 1.5 m. Only 4–7 lflt prs; fl shs under half lf length, fr curved. *D:* T; *Fl:* 5–8

Norwegian milk vetch

A. norvegicus

Erect, hrlss; 6–7 lflt prs. Fl shs 2 × length of lvs; fr flat, oval. *Ht:* 30 cm; *D:* T; *Fl:* 7–8

Crown vetch	Scorpion vetch	Lesser scorpion vetch
Coronilla varia	*C. coronata*	*C. minima*

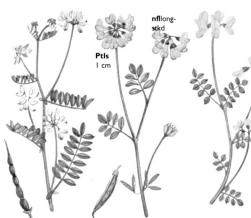

nfl long-stkd

Ptls 1 cm

Fr 4-angled

Fr to 3 cm

Spreading, hrlss; 7–12 lflt prs. Long-stkd infl, 10–20 fls. *Ht:* 1 m; *D:* T; *Fl:* 5–8

Stout, glaucous; 3–7 lflt prs; infl 12–20 fls; fr 4-angled. *Ht:* 60 cm; *D:* T; *Fl:* 5–7

Woody per. Leaflets unstkd, 2–6 prs. Infl of up to 15 fls, ptls to 8 mm. Pod 4-angled to 3.5 cm. *Ht:* 30 cm; *D:* SW; *Fl:* 4–6

Small scorpion vetch	Scorpion senna	Horseshoe vetch
C. vaginalis	*C. emerus*	*Hippocrepis comosa*

  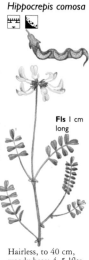

Ptls to 1 cm

Fls 1 cm long

Woody per to 50 cm. Oval, short-stkd lflts in 2–6 prs. Infl of 4–6 fls; pod to 3 cm long,000 has 6 angles and 4 wings. *D:* T; *Fl:* 5–6

Has 2–4 prs glaucous fine-pointed lflts, infl 2–6 fls, fr hangs. *Ht:* 80 cm; *D:* T; *Fl:* 4–6

Hairless, to 40 cm, woody base; 4–5 lflts, obovate. Fl sh long, infl of 5–8 flowers, fruit has horseshoe-shaped parts. *D:* W, C; *Fl:* 5–7

Meadow vetchling

Lathyrus pratensis

Clambers, angled shs, fine hrs; 1 pr pointed lflts, a tendril and arrow-shaped stipules. Fl stk long, fr flat. *Ht:* 1 m; *D:* T; *Fl:* 5–8

Yellow vetchling

L. aphaca

Hairless, to 1 m. No lflts but triangular stipules to 3 cm. Fls sol, long-stkd, long spl teeth, fr curved. *D:* W, C, S; *Fl:* 6–8

Grass vetchling

L. nissolia

Plant
hrlss

Erect to 90 cm; no lflts or tendrils but has grass-like shs. *D:* W, C, S; *Fl:* 5–7

Spring pea

L. vernus

Fls to 2 cm

Plant
perennial

Erect, usually hrlss. Stem angled, 2–4 lflt prs, no tendrils; infl 3–10 spaced fls, fr hrlss. *Ht:* 50 cm; *D:* T (not GB); *Fl:* 4–6

Narrow-leaved everlasting pea

L. sylvestris

Bushy, hrlss, winged stem; 1 lflt pr, single tendril; stipules thin, spread. Infl 3–8 fls, fr winged. *Ht:* 1.5 m; *D:* T (not N); *Fl:* 6–8

Bitter vetchling

L. linifolius

Tendrils
absent

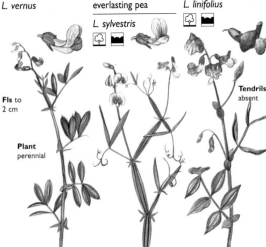

Rhizomatous; winged stem. Lflts narrow, 2–4 prs. Infl 2–8 fls, flat hrs on flower shs and spls. *Ht:* 30 cm; *D:* S, W, C; *Fl:* 6–7

Marsh pea

L. palustris

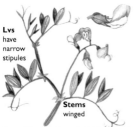

Lvs have narrow stipules

Stems winged

Scrambles to 1.2 m; 2–3 lflt prs and branched tendril per lf. Infl of 2–6 fls; fr flat. *D:* T; *Fl:* 5–7

Tuberous pea

L. tuberosus

Has rt tubers, stem angled; lvs have 1 lflt pr, 1 tendril; fr cylindrical. *Ht:* 1 m; *D:* T (not N); *Fl:* 6–7

Sea pea

L. japonicus

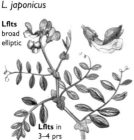

Lflts broad elliptic

Lflts in 3–4 prs

Low per, angled shs to 90 cm; has tendrils, stipules triangular, infl 5–15 fls, fr rigid. *D:* W, N; *Fl:* 6–8

Goat's rue

Galega officinalis

Stout, uprt; 4–8 lflt prs, arrow-shaped stipules. Fl shs equal lvs; fr straight. *D:* E, C, S; *Fl:* 6–7

Common melilot

Melilotus officinalis

Fl has short keel

Sprawling or uprt; many 6 mm fls, fr ribbed, hrlss, brown. *Ht:* 2 m; *D:* T; *Fl:* 7–9

White melilot

M. albus

Keel and wing ptls shorter than standard; fr hrlss, brown. *Ht:* 1 m; *D:* T; *Fl:* 7–8

Tall melilot

M. altissimus

Like *M. officinalis* but to 1.5 m. All ptls equal; fr hry, black. *D:* T (not E); *Fl:* 6–8

| Bladder senna | | Spotted medick | |

Colutea arborescens

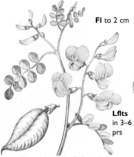

Fl to 2 cm

Lflts in 3–6 prs

Shrubby, v branched; lvs pinnate, stipules pointed. Infl of 3–8 fls, fr inflated. *Ht:* 4 m; *D:* S; *Fl:* 5–7

Medicago arabica

Lflts heart-shaped

Prostrate, hrlss; lflts toothed, in 3s, black blotch; 1–4 fls in infl; fr coiled. *Ht:* 45 cm; *D:* S, W; *Fl:* 4–8

| Black medick | | Sickle medick | |

M. lupulina

Infl dense, long-stkd

Prostrate; lflt tips notched with projecting nerve. Fr curled. *Ht:* 35 cm; *D:* T (not far N); *Fl:* 4–8

M. sativa ssp falcata

Lflts narrow to 1.5 cm

Scrambling; infl loose, each fl on sh longer than spls; fr curved. *Ht:* 50 cm; *D:* T (not N); *Fl:* 6–8

| Rest harrow | | Small rest harrow | |

Ononis repens

Creeping, no spines but sticky hrs; fl wings equal keel. *Ht:* 45 cm; *D:* W, C; *Fl:* 6–9

O. reclinata

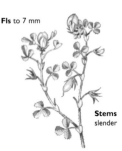

Fls to 7 mm

Stems slender

Sticky, uprt, no spines. Lflts v hry, fl shs bend back in fr. *Ht:* 7 cm; *D:* S, W; *Fl:* 6–7

Spiny rest harrow

O. spinosa

Large yellow rest harrow

O. natrix

Sainfoin

Onobrychis viciifolia

Pod hry

Lflts in
6–12 prs

Woody, uprt stems spiny with 2 lines of hrs; keel ptls longer than wings. *Ht:* 45 cm; *D:* W, C; *Fl:* 6–9

Dwarf shrub, stickily hry. Lvs variable, oval to narrow; infl loose, ptls veined. *Ht:* 45 cm; *D:* S, W; *Fl:* 5–8

Upright per; pinnate lvs, lflts narrow with pointed tips. Loose infl, to 50 fls. *Ht:* 60 cm; *D:* T; *Fl:* 6–8

Hedysarum

Hedysarum hedysaroides

Star-fruited fenugreek

Trigonella monspeliaca

Lflts oval, blunt, in 3–10 prs

Hairless; lvs pinnate; infl of 15–35 fls each 2 cm, colour varies. Drooping fr has a flange. *Ht:* 30 cm; *D:* S, C; *Fl:*7–8

Prostrate, hry; lvs 3-lobed, lflts obovate; fls 4 mm, unstkd; gps of 4–14. Fr just curved, hanging. *Ht:* 25 cm; *D:* C, S; *Fl:* 3–6

Petty whin ## German greenweed

Genista anglica

Fl 8 mm

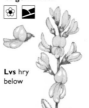

Shrub with spines to 2 cm, some curved; lvs hrlss, no stipules; spl tube 2-lipped. *Ht:* 45 cm; *D:* W; *Fl:* 5–6

G. germanica

Lvs hry below

Spiny, hry shrub to 60 cm. Infl loose, spls and fl shs very hairy, standard ptl pointed at tip. *D:* SW; *Fl:* 5–9

Dyer's greenwood

G. tinctoria

Fl 1.5 cm

Fr flat

Woody, uprt, no spines; shs grooved. Lvs hry below; infl long. *Ht:* 60 cm; *D:* T (not far N); *Fl:* 7–9

Broom

Cytisus scoparius

Pod 3 cm, hry

Fl stk 1 cm, hry

Erect hry shrub to 2 m, stems ridged; lvs 3-lobed, fall easily. Fl 2 cm. *D:* W, S, C; *Fl:* 5–6

Winged broom  ## Clustered broom

Chamaespartium sagittale

Mat-forming, fl shs broad-winged, lvs hry below, infl dense. *Ht:* 40 cm; *D:* C; *Fl:* 5–9

Chamaecytisus supinus

Fl to 2.5 cm

Fr 3 cm

Hairy but no spines; lvs 3-lobed. Infl of 2–8 fls, spls hry. *Ht:* 70 cm; *D:* C, S; *Fl:* 5–7

Gorse	Western dwarf gorse	Dwarf gorse
Ulex europaeus	*U. gallii*	*U. minor*

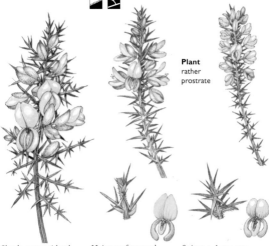

Plant rather prostrate

Shrub, many ridged spines to 2 cm, young plants have 3-lobed lvs. Spls hry. *Ht:* 1.5 m; *D:* W; *Fl:* 2–6

Hairy; unfurrowed spines *c.* 2 cm. Spls ⅔ ptl length, wings longer than keel. *Ht:* 60 cm; *D:* W; *Fl:* 7–9

Spines *c.* 1 cm, not furrowed. Spls as long as ptls, wings as long as keel. *Ht:* to 1 m; *D:* W; *Fl:* 7–9

Wood sorrel family Oxalidaceae

Herbs with a fleshy rootstock and often alternate, palmate leaves. The solitary or sparsely grouped flowers have 5 petals and sepals and 10 stamens. The fruit is a capsule.

Wood sorrel	Yellow oxalis
Oxalis acetosella	*O. corniculata*

Lf stks long, thin

Stems hry, rooting

Stk of each fl *c.* 1 cm

Creeping rhizomatous per. Lvs 3-lobed, lflts to 2 cm. Fls sol, to 3 cm on long thin stks. Fr to 4 mm. *Ht:* 10 cm; *D:* T; *Fl:* 4–6

Weak, prostrate. Lvs 3-lobed with small stipules, lflts deeply cut at tips. Long-stkd infl of 1–6 fls. *Ht:* 10 cm; *D:* S; *Fl:* 6–9

Geranium family Geraniaceae

Herbs or shrubs having alternate, lobed or compound leaves with stipules. Flowers have 5 separate petals and 5 sepals in a tube, which persists round the long-beaked fruit.

Bloody cranesbill | **Meadow cranesbill**

Geranium sanguineum | *G. pratense*

Bushy herb with creeping rhizome. Lvs in narrow segments with flat white hrs. Fls sol, to 3.6 cm, fr to 3 cm. *Ht:* 25 cm; *D:* T; *Fl:* 7–8

Perennial; erect hry stems. Lvs have deeply cut lobes. Paired fls on long stks which bend back in fr. Fr *c.* 2.5 cm. *Ht:* 50 cm; *D:* T; *Fl:* 6–9

Hedgerow cranesbill | **Shining cranesbill**

G. pyrenaicum | *G. lucidum*

 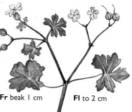

Fr beak 1 cm   **Fl** to 2 cm

Perennial with many sticky hrs. Fls in pairs. Fr stks bent back but tips erect. *Ht:* 40 cm; *D:* S, W; *Fl:* 6–8

Annual, branched from ground. Lvs glossy, reddish, cut to half lf width. Fls on spread, up-curved stks. *Ht:* 25 cm; *D:* T (not NE); *Fl:* 5–8

Herb Robert | **Wood cranesbill**

G. robertianum | *G. sylvaticum*

Ptls to 1.2 cm   **Ptls** to 1.8 cm

Biennial or ann. Shoots much-branched, delicate, reddish. Lvs lobed, lobes divided. Fl stks uprt. *Ht:* 30 cm; *D:* T (not far N); *Fl:* 5–9

Perennial; stems have sticky hrs above. Lvs hry, 7-lobed. Fls in pairs; fl stks erect in fruit. *Ht:* 50 cm; *D:* T; *Fl:* 6–7

Long-stalked cranesbill

G. columbinum

Fl stks long

Branching ann. Flat hrs on stems and spl veins. Fr hrlss. *Ht:* 30 cm; *D:* T (not far N); *Fl:* 6–7

Dove's-foot cranesbill

G. molle

Annual covered with soft white hrs. Lvs round. *Ht:* 30 cm; *D:* T (not far N); *Fl:* 4–9

Cut-leaved cranesbill

G. dissectum

Ptls to 5 mm

Straggling. Hrs on shs down-pointed, on spls sticky. *Ht:* 40 cm; *D:* T (not far N); *Fl:* 5–8

Marsh cranesbill

G. palustre

Ptls unnotched

Hairy per; lvs toothed. Few fls in infl. Fr stks bend back. *Ht:* 40 cm; *D:* T (not N); *Fl:* 7–8

Round-leaved cranesbill

G. rotundifolium

Much-branched annual, 5–9-lobed grey-green rounded lvs. Glandular, hairy. *Ht:* 10–40 cm; *D:* T except N; *Fl:* 6–7

Dusky cranesbill

G. phaeum

Erect perennial with glandular hairy stems. Fls in pairs. Dark petals pointed at tips, flattened or bent back. *Ht:* 30–60 cm; *D:* C, W; *Fl:* 5–6

Common storksbill

Erodium cicutarium

Hairy; lvs compound, lflts cut. Ptls longer than spls. *Ht:* 30 cm; *D:* T; *Fl:* 6–9

Sea storksbill

E. maritimum

Ptls to 4 mm

Flat ann; hrs bristly. Lvs lobed to half width. Fls sol or paired. *D:* NW; *Fl:* 5–9

Musk storksbill

E. moschatum

Plant smells of musk

Annual; many white hrs. Ptls just longer than spls. *Ht:* 30 cm; *D:* S, W; *Fl:* 5–7

Flax family Linaceae

Herbs with simple, usually alternate leaves without stipules. The flowers generally have 5 petals, sepals and stamens and an ovary with 3–5 cells. The fruit is a capsule that splits vertically.

Perennial flax

Linum perenne

Hairless perennial with rigid, upright stems. Numerous alternate leaves 1–2 cm long. Spls rounded, less than half fr length, ptls to 2 cm. Fr stks erect. A variable sp. *Ht:* 45 cm; *D:* C, E; *Fl:* 6–7

Pale flax

L. bienne

Hairless ann or per; stems uprt, branched. Ptls to 1.2 cm, spls oval, pointed tips, more than half fr length. Ancestor of cultivated flax. *Ht:* 45 cm; *D:* W, S; *Fl:* 5–9

Purging flax

L. catharticum

Delicate ann, slender stems. Lvs opposite, oval, rounded to 1.2 cm. Many fls in loose infl, fl shs fine, ptls 6 mm, spls pointed. Fr 3 mm, same length as spls. Seeds purgative. *Ht:* 15 cm; *D:* T; *Fl:* 6–9

Common flax

L. usitatissimum

Annual with erect branched stems (var cultivated for linseed oil). Lvs and petals larger than *L. bienne*. *Ht:* 40–85 cm; *D:* T; *Fl:* 5–7

Allseed

Radiola linoides

Tiny ann to 8 cm. Stems slender, branched, bushy. Lvs opp, 3 mm long. Fls *c.* 2 mm across in flat-topped clusters, have 4 ptls and spls. Fr spherical, *c.* 1 mm diam. *D:* T (not NE); *Fl:* 7–8

Spurge family Euphorbiaceae

Annual or perennial herbs with alternate leaves. Male and female flowers are usually separate but may be grouped together in a cup-like structure. The ovary has two or three cells.

Sea spurge

Euphorbia paralias

Lvs to 2 cm

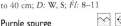

Stiff, hrlss, glaucous per; erect usually unbranched stems. Thick fleshy lvs have obscure midrib below. Fls in terminal clusters, ♂ and ♀ joined in a cup. Fr hrlss. *Ht:* to 40 cm; *D:* W, S; *Fl:* 8–11

Wood spurge

E. amygdaloides

Robust, hry per to 80 cm. Lvs on veg shs taper to stk at base, lvs on fl shs do not. Infl a 5–10 rayed umbel with kidney-shaped bracts below. *D:* NW, C, S; *Fl:* 3–5

Portland spurge

E. portlandica

Like a small version of *E. paralias* but stems unbranched. Lvs fleshy, prominent midrib below, tapered to base. Often reddens with age. *Ht:* 25 cm; *D:* W; *Fl:* 5–9

Purple spurge

E. peplis

Prostrate ann, usually with 4 main branches from base. Lvs to 1 cm, enlarged on one side at base and with divided stipules. Infl to 2 mm long; fr a hairless, 3-sided capsule. *Ht:* 4 cm; *D:* T; *Fl:* 7–9

Dwarf spurge

E. exigua

Hairless, glaucous, to 30 cm. Lvs to 3 cm, untoothed, narrow, tips pointed. Infl an umbel with 3 rays, bracts below lvs broader than true lvs. *D:* T (not E); *Fl:* 6–10

Petty spurge

Euphorbia peplus

Hairless ann, stem simple or branched. Lvs to 3 cm, oval, untoothed. Infl a 3-rayed umbel with stklss bracts. *Ht:* 30 cm; *D:* T; *Fl:* 4–11

Sun spurge

E. helioscopia

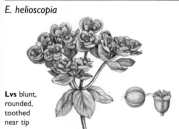

Lvs blunt, rounded, toothed near tip

Hairless, uprt, few brs. Infl 5-rayed, bracts round at base. *Ht:* 35 cm; *D:* T; *Fl:* 5–10

Caper spurge

E. lathyris

Lvs to 2 cm

Glaucous, hrlss; lvs opp, broad, round at base. Infl 2–6 brs, fr to 2 cm. *Ht:* 1m; *D:* S, W, C; *Fl:* 6–7

Annual mercury

Mercurialis annua

Neat hrlss; erect shs v branched; lvs stkd. ♂ and ♀ plants separate, ♂ fls in spike, ♀ sol, unstkd. *Ht:* 40 cm; *D:* T; *Fl:* 7–10

Dog's mercury

M. perennis

Lvs to 8 cm, short-stkd

Patch-forming, hry. Shs uprt, no brs. ♂ and ♀ plants separate, ♂ fls clustered, stkd, ♀ sol, long-stkd. *Ht:* 30 cm; *D:* T; *Fl:* 2–4

Cypress spurge

E. cyparissias

Lvs narrow to 3 cm

Has rhizome; dense shs hrlss, often branched. Many alt lvs. Infl of 5–9 brs. *Ht:* 20 cm; *D:* T (not far N); *Fl:* 5–8

Rue family Rutaceae

Herbs or shrubs with glandular leaves. The flowers have 4–5 free sepals and petals, 8 or 10 stamens and free styles.

Rue

Ruta graveolens

Strong-smelling hrlss per to 45 cm. Lower lvs stkd, v divided. Infl loose, spls narrow, pointed, ptls toothed. *D:* S, SC; *Fl:* 5–7

Milkwort family Polygalaceae

Herbs with simple leaves which have no stipules. Asymmetrical flowers have 5 sepals (two petal-like) and 3–5 petals.

Common milkwort   ## Chalk milkwort

Polygala vulgaris ### *P. calcarea*

Infl loose, fls to 8 mm

Scrambling stems, lvs narrow, alt to 1 cm at base, 3 cm above. Colour variable. *Ht:* 20 cm; *D:* T; *Fl:* 5–9

Prostrate per. Lvs in rosette to 2 cm, glossy, obovate, top lvs smaller. *Ht:* 15 cm; *D:* W; *Fl:* 5–7

Shrubby milkwort   ## Thyme-leaved milkwort

P. chamaebuxus ### *P. serpyllifolia*

Lvs to 3 cm

Infl of 3–8 fls

Dwarf shrub to 15 cm. Lvs oval or linear; fls sol or in prs, long-keeled. *D:* WC; *Fl:* 4–9

Like *P. vulgaris* but lower lvs in opp prs, upper alt. More compact infl. *Ht:* 20 cm; *D:* W, C; *Fl:* 5–8

Balsam family Balsaminaceae

Herbs with no stipules at their leaf bases. The flowers have 3 or 5 sepals which are often petal-like and 5 petals, the upper one large and the lower ones united in two pairs. The ovary develops into a 5-celled, many-seeded fruit.

Himalayan balsam

Impatiens glandulifera

Erect, robust annual 1–2 m high. Stem stout, translucent and reddish. Leaves opposite or in groups of 3 around stem, stalked and sharply toothed. Flowers to 4 cm across with short, bent spurs and 3 sepals borne in groups of 5–10 at shoot tips. *D:* T; *Fl:* 7–10

Touch-me-not balsam

I. noli-tangere

Orange balsam

I. capensis

Like *I. noli-tangere* but lvs to 8 cm with fewer, smaller teeth. Fl spur curved. *Ht:* to 80 cm; *D:* W; *Fl:* 6–8

Small balsam

I. parviflora

Upright hrlss ann. Lvs to 12 cm stkd with teeth to 3 mm. Fls to 4 cm grouped in lf axils; have 3 spls, the lowest with a curved spur. Name comes from seeds which shoot out if fruit is touched. *Ht:* 40 cm; *D:* T (not far N); *Fl:* 7–9

Annual to 1 m. Lvs alternate with many teeth. Fls *c.* 1 cm, spur straight. *D:* T (not Scand); *Fl:* 7–11

74

Mallow family Malvaceae

Herbs and shrubs with leaves often palmately lobed. Grouped or single flowers have 5 free petals and 5 sepals either free or joined and often with an extra outer sepal whorl (epicalyx).

Common mallow

Malva sylvestris

Hairy perennial herb. Basal lvs rounded, lobed to 10 cm across. Fls to 4 cm in diam, clustered in lf axils. Epicalyx has 3 oval lobes. *Ht:* to 90 cm; *D:* T (not far N); *Fl:* 6-9

Dwarf mallow

M. neglecta

Often prostrate; lvs to 7 cm diam. Epicalyx 3-lobed. *Ht:* 40 cm; *D:* T (not far N); *Fl:* 6-9

Tree mallow

Lavatera arborea

Musk mallow

M. moschata

Leaves deeply cut. Fls sol to 6 cm. Epicalyx 3-lobed. *Ht:* 60 cm; *D:* T (not N); *Fl:* 7–8

Marsh mallow

Althaea officinalis

Softly hry. Short-stkd fls to 4 cm. Epicalyx 6-lobed. *Ht:* 1 m; *D:* T (not N); *Fl:* 8–9

Tall, erect, woody biennial. Lvs softly hairy, shallow, 5–7-lobed. Petals pale with darker veins. *Ht:* 60 cm– 3 m; *D:* W; *Fl:* 7–9

Thymelaea family Thymelaeaceae

Shrubs with alternate, unlobed leaves with no stipules. Flowers have 4 or 5 lobed sepals placed at the end of the enlarged, tube-shaped, petal-like flower stalks.

Spurge laurel	Mezereon	Annual thymelaea
Daphne laureola	*D. mezereum*	*Thymelaea passerina*

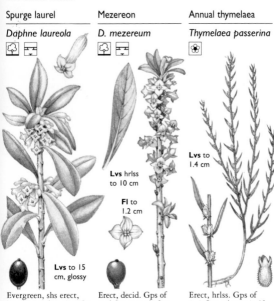

Evergreen, shs erect, lvs clustered at tips; fls 1 cm, 8 stms, 4 spls, infl 5–10 fls; fr 1.2 cm, black. *Ht:* 70 cm; *D:* S, W; *Fl:* 2–4

Erect, decid. Gps of 2–4 fls appear before lvs over old lf scars; 4 spls equal tube in length; fr 1 cm, red. *Ht:* 65 cm; *D:* C, S; *Fl:* 2–4

Erect, hrlss. Gps of 1–3 fls to 4 mm in lf axils with 2 tiny bracts and tuft of hrs, spls blunt. *Ht:* 35 cm; *D:* S, W, C; *Fl:* 7–10

St John's wort family Clusiaceae

Herbs or shrubs with simple opposite leaves, often with resinous glands. The flowers have 5 petals and sepals and many stamens.

Perforate St John's wort

Hypericum perforatum

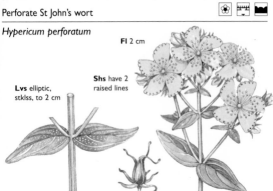

Erect, hrlss. Lvs show translucent glands if held to light. Spls half ptl length, no black glands at edge. *Ht:* 70 cm; *D:* T (not far N); Fl: 6–9

Slender St John's wort

H. pulchrum

Shs uprt | **Lvs** to 1 cm

Translucent glands on lvs; spls round, under half ptl length, black glands at edge. *Ht:* 45 cm; *D:* NW; *Fl:* 6–8

Hairy St John's wort

H. hirsutum

Fl 1.5 cm

Shs uprt

Hairy, few brs; infl of many fls, spls half ptl length have black glands. *Ht:* 70 cm; *D:* T (not NE); *Fl:* 7–8

Trailing St John's wort

H. humifusum

Spls almost equal ptls

Prostrate per, delicate stems to 20 cm, 2 raised lines; translucent glands on lvs. Few 1 cm fls in infl, spl size varies. *D:* W, C; *Fl:* 6–9

Marsh St John's wort

H. elodes

Fl 1.5 cm

Very hry, few fls in infl, spls fine-toothed, stamens in 3 gps. *Ht:* 20 cm; *D:* W; *Fl:* 6–9

Tutsan

H. androsaemum

Fl 2 cm

Stem has 2 lines; spls unequal, stamens long, fr a berry. *Ht:* 70 cm; *D:* W; *Fl:* 6–8

Square-stemmed St John's wort

H. tetrapterum

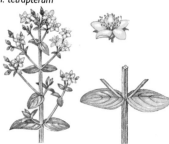

Upright, hrlss per, stems 4-ridged, lvs to 2 cm. Many 1 cm fls in infl, spls narrow, pointed, ⅔ ptl length. *Ht:* 55 cm; *D:* T (not far N); *Fl:* 6–9

Violet family Violaceae

Herbs whose leaves have stipules. Often spurred, solitary flowers have parts in fives and 2 bracts on their stalks.

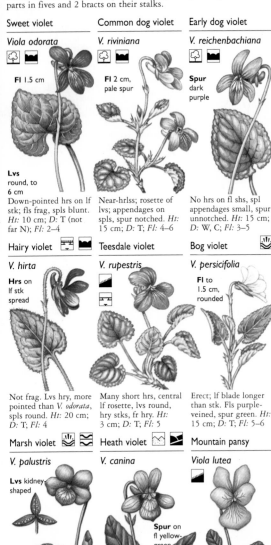

Sweet violet

Viola odorata

Fl 1.5 cm

Lvs round, to 6 cm

Down-pointed hrs on lf stk; fls frag, spls blunt. *Ht:* 10 cm; *D:* T (not far N); *Fl:* 2–4

Common dog violet

V. riviniana

Fl 2 cm, pale spur

Near-hrlss; rosette of lvs; appendages on spls, spur notched. *Ht:* 15 cm; *D:* T; *Fl:* 4–6

Early dog violet

V. reichenbachiana

Spur dark purple

No hrs on fl shs, spl appendages small, spur unnotched. *Ht:* 15 cm; *D:* W, C; *Fl:* 3–5

Hairy violet

V. hirta

Hrs on lf stk spread

Not frag. Lvs hry, more pointed than *V. odorata*, spls round. *Ht:* 20 cm; *D:* T; *Fl:* 4

Teesdale violet

V. rupestris

Many short hrs, central lf rosette, lvs round, hry stks, fr hry. *Ht:* 3 cm; *D:* T; *Fl:* 5

Bog violet

V. persicifolia

Fl to 1.5 cm, rounded

Erect; lf blade longer than stk. Fls purple-veined, spur green. *Ht:* 15 cm; *D:* T; *Fl:* 5–6

Marsh violet

V. palustris

Lvs kidney-shaped

No uprt stems, lf blade to 4 cm. Fls 1 cm, ptls pale, dark veins, spls blunt. *D:* T; *Fl:* 4–7

Heath violet

V. canina

Spur on fl yellow-green

Creeping per, no lf rosette. Lvs not as notched at base as other spp. *Ht:* 20 cm; *D:* T; *Fl:* 4–6

Mountain pansy

Viola lutea

Slender creeping per with sol stems. Stipules deeply lobed; fls large yellow. *Ht:* 7–20 cm; *D:* W, C; *Fl:* 4–8

78

Wild pansy	Field pansy

V. tricolor

V. arvensis

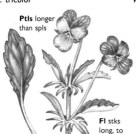

Ptls longer than spls

Ptls shorter than spls

Fl stks long, to 8 cm

Stipules lobed, centre lobe not indented; spur longer than sepal appendages. *Ht:* 30 cm; *D:* T; *Fl:* 4–9

Centre stipule lobe indented. Spur equals spl appendages, fl less than 2 cm. *Ht:* 30 cm; *D:* T; *Fl:* 4–10

Rockrose family Cistaceae

Shrubs or herbs with opposite, hairy, unlobed leaves. Flowers have 3 or 5 sepals, 5 petals and many stamens.

Common rockrose

White rockrose

Helianthemum nummularium

H. apenninum

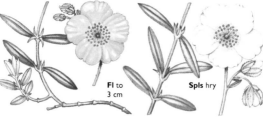

Fl to 3 cm

Spls hry

Straggles to 30 cm. Lvs stipuled, woolly below. Infl loose, style not bent. *D:* T (not far N); *Fl:* 6–9

Like *H. nummularium* except in fl col. Lvs woolly all over, curled edges. *Ht:* 25 cm; *D:* SW; *Fl:* 5–7

Hoary rockrose	Spotted rockrose	Common fumana

H. canum

Tuberaria guttata

Fumana procumbens

Fl to 1.5 cm

Ptls have spot

Leaves small, oval, no stipules; small fl, bent style. *Ht:* 10 cm; *D:* C, S; *Fl:* 5–7

Erect; hry lvs unstkd, stipuled, terminal infl, no styles. *Ht:* 20 cm; *D:* S, W; *Fl:* 5–8

Prostrate, brs 30 cm; lvs alt, no stipules; fls sol, stks as long as lvs. *D:* S, W; *Fl:* 5

Water chestnut family Trapaceae

Annual aquatics with large woody fruits. Leaves in a rosette have inflated stalks. Flower parts are in fours.

Water chestnut

Trapa natans   **Floating lf blades** to 4 cm

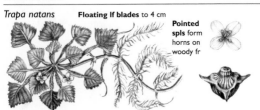

Pointed spls form horns on woody fr

Robust submerged stems, unbranched, to 2 m. Lf stks to 17 cm, hry, swollen. Fls in lf axils, ptls 8 mm. Locally cultivated. *D:* S, C; *Fl:* 6–7

Willowherb family Onagraceae

Annuals or perennials. Single or terminally grouped flowers usually have 4 unjoined petals and sepals, and 8 stamens.

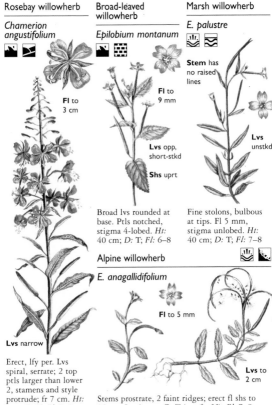

Rosebay willowherb

Chamerion angustifolium

Fl to 3 cm

Lvs narrow

Erect, lfy per. Lvs spiral, serrate; 2 top ptls larger than lower 2, stamens and style protrude; fr 7 cm. *Ht:* 1 m; *D:* T; *Fl:* 7–9

Broad-leaved willowherb

Epilobium montanum

Fl to 9 mm

Lvs opp, short-stkd

Shs uprt

Broad lvs rounded at base. Ptls notched, stigma 4-lobed. *Ht:* 40 cm; *D:* T; *Fl:* 6–8

Alpine willowherb

E. anagallidifolium

Fl to 5 mm

Lvs to 2 cm

Stems prostrate, 2 faint ridges; erect fl shs to 10 cm. Lvs in prs. *D:* T (not far N); *Fl:* 7–8

Marsh willowherb

E. palustre

Stem has no raised lines

Lvs unstkd

Fine stolons, bulbous at tips. Fl 5 mm, stigma unlobed. *Ht:* 40 cm; *D:* T; *Fl:* 7–8

Great willowherb

E. hirsutum

Fl 2 cm

Very hry; stigma 4-lobed, longer than stms. *Ht:* 1.2 m; *D:* T (not far N); *Fl:* 7–8

Large-flowered evening primrose

Oenothera glazioviana

Robust, stem hry to 1 m, lvs spiral, buds big, ridged, spls red striped, 4 ptls to 5 cm. *D:* W, C; *Fl:*6–9

Hoary willowherb

E. parviflorum

Fl under 1 cm

Plant softly hry

Leaves do not run into stem; 4-lobed stigma equals stms. *Ht:* 80 cm; *D:* T (not far N); *Fl:* 7–8

Enchanter's nightshade

Circaea lutetiana

Has stolons and few hrs; 2 deep-notched ptls and spls. *Ht:* 50 cm; *D:* T; *Fl:* 6–8

Hampshire purslane

American willowherb

E. ciliatum

Fl to 6 mm

Lvs to 10 cm

Stem hry, 4 raised lines; lvs short-stalked, stigma unlobed. *Ht:* 80 cm; *D:* NW; *Fl:* 6–8

Alpine enchanter's nightshade

C. alpina

Fr hooked

Lvs opp, stkd

Has tuberous stock; fl shs space out in fr, ptls notched. *Ht:* 20 cm; *D:* N; *Fl:* 7–8

Ludwigia palustris

Lvs to 2 cm in opp prs

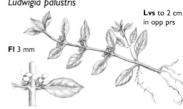

Fl 3 mm

Aquatic, shs slender to 30 cm. Fls sol in axils, 4 spread spls, no ptls. *D:* W, C, S; *Fl:* 6

Sea-heath family Frankeniaceae

Dwarf shrubs with opposite leaves. Flowers have 4–6 sepals and petals and 6 stamens. The fruit is a capsule.

Sea-heath

Frankenia laevis

Fl 5 mm, 5 ptls and spls, 6 stamens

Delicate mat-forming, prostrate woody per resembling spp of *Erica* (p. 93). Lvs densely crowded. *Ht:* to 15 cm; *D:* W; *Fl:* 7–8

Cucumber family Cucurbitaceae

Mostly succulent, tendrilled, hairy annual climbers. Flowers have parts in fives and petals often joined at the base.

White bryony

Bryonia dioica
Stems bristly, angled, branched near base

Fl to 2 cm

Fr a red berry

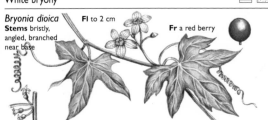

Scrambles to 3 m. Tendrils arise from stem near lvs. ♂, ♀ fls on separate plants, veined ptls longer than spls, 3 stigmas 2 × cut. *D:* S, W; *Fl:* 5–9

Loosestrife family Lythraceae

Herbs or shrubs with whorled leaves without stipules. The petals are joined to the sepals which are united in a tube.

Purple loosestrife | Grass poly

Lythrum salicaria

Fl to 1.5 cm

L. hyssopifolia

Lvs unstkd to 1.5 cm

Infl a spike to 30 cm

Stem 4-angled; lvs unstkd, opp or in whorls of 3. Fls have 4–6 ptls. *Ht:* 1 m; *D:* T (not far N); *Fl:* 6–8

Much branched, hrlss. Fls 5 mm, sol in lf axils, 6 stamens. *Ht:* 15 cm; *D:* S, W, C; *Fl:* 6–7

Water-milfoil family Haloragaceae
Marestail family Hippuridaceae

Aquatics, often with whorled leaves. Solitary marestail flowers have no sepals or petals and one stamen. Water-milfoil flowers have tiny petals and sepals and 8 stamens.

Spiked water-milfoil   Whorled water-milfoil

Myriophyllum spicatum   *M. verticillatum*

Lvs 25–35 lobes, 5 per whorl

Branched, submerged shs to 2.5 m. Lvs 4 per whorl, 13–35 narrow lobes, fl bracts entire. *D:* T; *Fl:* 6–7

Submerged shs to 3 m. Fl spike to 25 cm, above water; fls in whorls of 5, bracts pinnate. *D:* T; *Fl:* 7–8

Alternate-leaved water-milfoil   Marestail

M. alterniflorum

Lvs to 2.5 cm, 6–18 lobes, in whorls of 4

Stems branched, slender

Submerged shs to 1.2 m. Fl spike droops in bud, fls in whorls. ♀ at base, ♂ above; bracts pinnate below, simple above. *D:* W, C, N; *Fl:* 5–8

Hippuris vulgaris

Emergent with rhizome. Lvs unlobed in whorls of 6–12. *Ht:* 60 cm; *D:* T; *Fl:* 6–7

Dogwood family Cornaceae

Mostly trees and shrubs rather than herbs. Flowers have parts in fours (the sepals are small) above the ovary.

Dwarf cornel

Cornus suecica

Fr 5 mm

Perennial, shs erect. Lvs in opp prs, parallel veins. Infl an umbel of 8–25 fls to 2 mm with 4 bracts to 8 mm. *Ht:* 15 cm; *D:* N; *Fl:* 7–8

Ivy family Araliaceae

Evergreen woody climbers. Flowers in umbels have sepals joined in a 5-toothed tube and 5 petals and stamens.

Ivy

Hedera helix

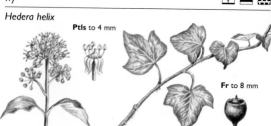

Ptls to 4 mm

Fr to 8 mm

Climbs to 30 m, using rts on trees. Lvs hrlss, 3–5 lobes; infl gps of umbels on climbing shs only, fr berry-like. *D:* W, C, S; *Fl:* 9–11

Carrot family Apiaceae

Herbs, often with hollow, furrowed stems. Leaves have sheathing stalks. Flowers, in groups of umbels with bracts and/or bracteoles, have parts in fives and sepals united in a tube.

Hogweed

Heracleum sphondylium

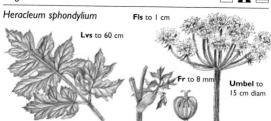

Fls to 1 cm

Lvs to 60 cm

Fr to 8 mm

Umbel to 15 cm diam

Bristly, stems hollow; lvs 1-pinnate. Bracteoles but no bracts in infl, outer fls have unequal ptls. *Ht:* 1.5 m; *D:* T (not far N); *Fl:* 6–9

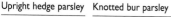

Upright hedge parsley	Knotted bur parsley	Spreading bur parsley
Torilis japonica	*T. nodosa*	*T. arvensis*

Stems solid

Stems solid

Fr 4 mm

Fr to 3 mm

Fr to 5 mm

Umbel 5–15 rays, 4–6 bracts, hooked spines on fr. *Ht:* 1 m; *D:* T (not far N); *Fl:* 7–8

Short-stkd umbel, no bracts, long bracteoles. Fr spines straight. *Ht:* 20 cm; *D:* S, W; *Fl:* 5–7

Umbel 3–5 rays, 1 or no bracts, spines on fr curved. *Ht:* 25 cm; *D:* W, S, C; *Fl:* 7–9

Cow parsley	Bur chervil	Greater bur parsley

Anthriscus sylvestris

A. caucalis

Turgenia latifolia

Umbel
long-stkd,
2–5 rays

Stems
hrlss all
over

Fr 3 mm

Fr to 1 cm

Umbel 4–10 rays, no hrs or bracts; fr to 5 mm, smooth. *Ht:* 80 cm; *D:* T; *Fl:* 4–6

Umbel has bracteoles, no bracts; spines on fr hooked. *Ht:* 35 cm; *D:* W, C, S; *Fl:* 5–6

Leaves 1-pinnate, hry below; fr has rows of spines. *Ht:* 45 cm; *D:* S, C; *Fl:* 5–8

Small bur parsley	Stone parsley	Cambridge milk parsley

Caucalis platycarpos

Sison amomum

Selinum carvifolia

Lvs
hrlss

Sepal tube has obvious teeth; fr has spineless ridges. *Ht:* 20 cm; *D:* T (not far N); *Fl:* 6–7

Fetid smell, hrlss; umbel 3–6 rays, fr round. *Ht:* 80 cm; *D:* S, W; *Fl:* 7–9

Stems solid, hrlss, winged ridges; no spl teeth; fr 4 mm. *Ht:* 80 cm; *D:* T; *Fl:* 7–10

Rough chervil	Hemlock	Coriander

Chaerophyllum temulentum

Conium maculatum

Coriandrum sativum

Umbel
3–5 rays

Stems bristly, spotted; bracts reflexed in fr, fr tapered. *Ht:* 80 cm; *D:* T (not N); *Fl:* 6–7

Stems spotted; infl 10–20 rays, fr 3 mm, wavy ridges. *Ht:* 2 m; *D:* T (not N); *Fl:* 6–7

Leaves 1–2 pinnate; ptls vary in size, frs stick in groups. *Ht:* 55 cm; *D:* S; *Fl:* 6

Pignut	Great pignut	Fool's parsley

Conopodium majus | *Bunium bulbocastanum* | *Aethusa cynapium*

Hairless, hollow stem. Umbels to 7 cm, 6–12 rays. Fr 4 mm has prominent uprt styles; tubers edible. *Ht:* 40 cm; *D:* W; *Fl:* 5–6

Stem solid. Fr to 3 mm has curved, short styles. *Ht:* 50 cm; *D:* S, C; *Fl:* 6–7

Umbel 10–20 rays, 3–4 bracteoles on outer part, no bracts; fr to 4 mm. *Ht:* 1 m; *D:* T; *Fl:* 7–8

Wild carrot	Moon carrot

Daucus carota | *Seseli libanotis*

Infl to 7 cm diam

Bristly, stem solid, many rays in infl, bracts lobed; fr ridged, spiny. *Ht:* 80 cm; *D:* T; *Fl:* 6–8

Stems have fibrous base. Umbels long-stkd to 6 cm diam, many bracts and bracteoles. *Ht:* 45 cm; *D:* T (not far N); *Fl:* 7–8

Caraway	Whorled caraway	Honewort

Carum carvi | *C. verticillatum* | *Trinia glauca*

Plant glaucous

Lvs fine-lobed

Leaves 2-pinnate. No bracts or bracteoles; fr strong smelling. *Ht:* 40 cm; *D:* T; *Fl:* 6–7

Leaves 1-pinnate, look whorled. Some bracts and bracteoles. *Ht:* 45 cm; *D:* W; *Fl:* 7–8

Male umbels 1 cm, ♀ 3 cm on separate plants. *Ht:* 15 cm; *D:* W, C, S; *Fl:* 5–6

Greater water parsnip

Sium latifolium

Fr 3
mm

Leaves 1-pinnate, 4–6 lflt prs, serrate; infl 20+ rays; fr oval. *Ht:* 1.5 m; *D:* T; *Fl:* 7–8

Lesser water parsnip

Berula erecta

Lflts
serrate

Leaves 1-pinnate, 7–10 lflt prs; infl 10–20 rays. *Ht:* to 1 m; *D:* T (not far N); *Fl:* 7–9

Spignel

Meum anthamaticum

Aromatic, lf segments fine; umbel 6–15 rays; fr to 1 cm. *Ht:* 45 cm; *D:* W, C; *Fl:* 6–7

Angelica

Angelica sylvestris

Stems have bloom (unlike *A. archangelica*); lvs 2–3pinnate, stks inflated. *Ht:* 1.5 m; *D:* T; *Fl:* 7–9

Cowbane

Cicuta virosa

Plant v poisonous

Leaflets narrow, serrate. Many bracteoles longer than fl stks. *Ht:* to 1.3 m; *D:* T; *Fl:* 7–8

Sermountain

Laserpitium latifolium

Lflts hry
below

Umbel has many bracts, few bracteoles. Fr to 1 cm has wavy wings. *Ht:* 1.2 m; *D:* T (not UK); *Fl:* 6–8

Sweet cicely

Myrrhis odorata

Strongly aromatic. Some fls ♂ only; fr to 2.5 cm. *Ht:* to 1 m; *D:* W, mts in S; *Fl:* 5–6

87

Corn parsley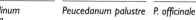
Milk parsley
Hog's fennel

Petroselinum segetum

Peucedanum palustre

P. officinale

Lower brs spreading; lvs 1-pinnate, umbels irregular. *Ht:* to 1 m; *D:* W; *Fl:* 8–9

Umbel has 4 bracts bent back, long thin bracteoles. *Ht:* to 1.5 m; *D:* T; *Fl:* 7–9

Linear, tangled lflts; infl 20+ rays, often no bracteoles. *Ht:* 1 m; *D:* S, C; *Fl:* 7–9

Field eryngo
Sea holly

Eryngium campestre

E. maritimum

Fl 8 mm

Basal lvs pinnate, stkd. Bracts spiny, bracteoles 2–3 × fl length. *Ht:* 45 cm; *D:* C, S; *Fl:* 7–8

Glaucous. Bracts spiny, toothed, bracteoles just longer than fls. *Ht:* 45 cm; *D:* T; *Fl:* 7–8

Rock samphire
Burnet saxifrage
Greater burnet-saxifrage

Crithmum maritimum

Pimpinella saxifraga

P. major

Stems flexible

Fleshy per to 30 cm. Lf segs cylindrical; many bracts and bracteoles in umbel. Fr to 6 mm, egg-shaped. *D:* T (not N); *Fl:* 6–8

Basal lvs 1-pinnate, stem lvs 2-pinnate; no bracts or bracteoles. *Ht:* 1 m; *D:* T; *Fl:* 7–8

Stems rigid, brittle; lvs 1-pinnate; no bracts or bracteoles. *Ht:* 1 m; *D:* T; *Fl:* 6–7

Ground elder

Shepherd's needle

Aegopodium podagraria

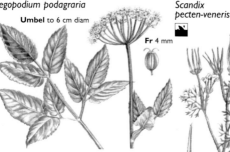

Umbel to 6 cm diam

Fr 4 mm

Scandix pecten-veneris

Creeps to 1 m. Lf segments *c.* 5 cm long, serrate.
No bracts or bracteoles. *D:* T; *Fl:* 5–7

Umbels 2-3 rays;
bracteoles lobed, 1 cm;
fr ridged. *Ht:* 35 cm;
D: W, C, S; *Fl:* 4–7

Hemlock water dropwort

Parsley water dropwort

Water dropwort

Oenanthe crocata

O. lachenalii

Lflts linear

O. fistulosa

Has rt tubers; lvs 3–4
pinnate to 50 cm; v
poisonous. *Ht:* 1.2 m;
D: W; *Fl:* 6–7

Pinnate part of lf
longer than solid stk.
Fr 2 mm, stk swollen.
Ht: 1 m; *D:* W; *Fl:* 6–9

Pinnate part of lf
shorter than hollow
stk. *Ht:* 45 cm; *D:* W,
C, S; *Fl:* 7–9

Fine-leaved water dropwort

Wild celery

Fool's watercress

O. aquatica

Umbel short-stkd

Lvs 3-pinnate

Apium graveolens

A. nodiflorum

Roots fibrous; lower lvs
submerged, umbels
opp lvs. *Ht:* 1.2 m; *D:*
T (not far N); *Fl:* 6–9

Top stem lvs 3-lobed,
no bracts or bracteoles;
celery smell. *Ht:* 40
cm; *D:* T; *Fl:* 6–8

Often prostrate to 1 m;
umbels unstkd, no
bracts, 5 bracteoles. *D:*
T; *Fl:* 7–8

Sickle hare's ear	Scots lovage

Bupleurum falcatum

Hollow-stemmed per; bracteoles shorter than fls. *Ht:* to 1.3 m; *D:* S, C, E; *Fl:* 7–10

Smallest hare's ear

B. tenuissimum

Plant annual

Umbels to 5 mm in lf axils; fls shorter than bracteoles. *Ht:* 35 cm; *D:* S, W, C; *Fl:* 7–9

Giant hogweed

Heracleum mantegazzianum

Massive hollow purple-spotted stems to 5.5 m high containing irritant sap. Lvs to 2.5 m, lobed with pointed tips, softly hairy. *D:* W; *Fl:* 6–7

Scots lovage

Ligusticum scoticum

Fr 4 mm

Hairless per to 90 cm. Upper lvs 3-lobed, serrate, basal lvs 2-pinnate. *D:* N; *Fl:* 7

Fennel

Foeniculum vulgare

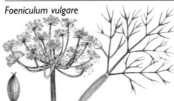

Glaucous, strong smell. Lvs cut into v fine segs. *Ht:* 1 m; *D:* T (not N); *Fl:* 7–10

Alexanders

Smyrnium olusatrum

Lf stks sheathing, inflated

Leaves pinnate, shiny with 3-lobed segs; fr 8 mm, black. *Ht:* to 1.5 m; *D:* S; *Fl:* 4–6

Marsh pennywort

Hydrocotyle vulgaris

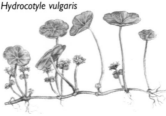

Creeping per. Lvs circular to 5 cm diam on long erect stks to 25 cm. *D:* W, C, S; *Fl:* 7–10

Pepper saxifrage	Astrantia	

Silaum silaus

Astrantia major

Bracts linear to 2 cm, whitish below

Hairless per; lvs 2–3 pinnate, fine-toothed segs. *Ht:* to 1 m; *D:* W, C, E; *Fl:* 6–8

Has creeping stock. Basal lvs to 15 cm, palmate; some fls ♂ only. *Ht:* 60 cm; *D:* C; *Fl:* 5–7

Sanicle	Wild parsnip	Bladderseed

Sanicula europaea

Pastinaca sativa

Physospermum cornubiense

Hairless per to 60 cm; basal lvs round to 6 cm, 3–5 lobes; fr 3 mm. *D:* T; *Fl:* 5–9

Leaves 1-pinnate, shs hollow; fr to 8 mm, pointed. *Ht:* 1.2 m; *D:* T (not far N); *Fl:* 7–8

Leaves and umbels long-stkd; fr 5 mm, styles bent back. *Ht:* 55 cm; *D:* S; *Fl:* 7–8

Diapensia family Diapensiaceae

Arctic perennials and dwarf shrubs. Sepals and petals are in a 5-lobed tube, the stigma is 3-lobed.

Diapensia

Diapensia lapponica

Ptls I cm

Lvs to I cm

Woody, cushion-forming per to 5 cm. Lvs unlobed, narrowing to short stk. Fls sol, fl stks to 3 cm. Spl tube 5 mm. *D:* N; *Fl:* 5–6

Wintergreen family Pyrolaceae

Perennial evergreen herbs with rhizomes. The symmetrical flowers have parts in fives and the petals are not united in a tube. The 5-celled ovary has a single stigma.

Common wintergreen

Pyrola minor

Creeping; lvs alt, short-stkd. Fls spherical, style straight, stigma 5-lobed. *Ht:* 20 cm; *D:* T; *Fl:* 6–8

Round-leaved wintergreen

P. rotundifolia

Fl 1.2 cm

Leaves alt, stk longer than blade. Long, curved style makes ring under stigma. *Ht:* 25 cm; *D:* T; *Fl:* 7–9

Yellow wintergreen

P. chlorantha

Like *P. rotundifolia* but lvs pale above, obovate; fls yellow-green. *Ht:* 20 cm; *D:* T (not W); *Fl:* 7–9

Umbellate wintergreen

Chimaphila umbellata

Leaves serrate, appear whorled; fls in an umbel, v short styles, ptls spread. *Ht:* 20 cm; *D:* N, C, E; *Fl:* 6–7

One-flowered wintergreen

Moneses uniflora

Fl 1.5 cm

Leaves opp, rounded, short-stkd. Fl shs to 15 cm; fls, sol wide-open. *D:* T; *Fl:* 6–8

Toothed wintergreen

Orthilia secunda

Leaves serrate; fl shs 10 cm, fls all to one side, stigmas projecting. *D:* T; *Fl:* 7–8

Yellow birdsnest

Monotropa hypopitys

Fl hry inside

Has no green parts. Waxy stems to 30 cm, fls drooping, fr erect. *D:* T; *Fl:* 6–8

Heather family Ericaceae

Dwarf shrubs with simple evergreen leaves. The flowers, usually in clusters, have petals fused into a tube to which the stamens are not attached and a single style.

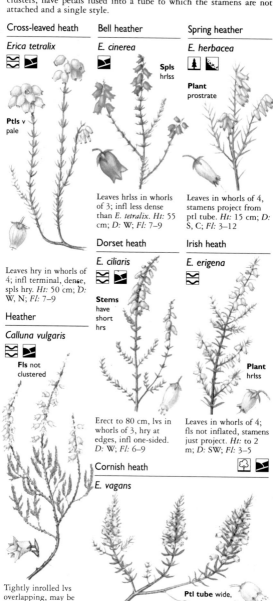

Cross-leaved heath

Erica tetralix

Ptls v pale

Leaves hry in whorls of 4; infl terminal, dense, spls hry. *Ht:* 50 cm; *D:* W, N; *Fl:* 7–9

Heather

Calluna vulgaris

Fls not clustered

Tightly inrolled lvs overlapping, may be hry; 4 bracteoles at base of each fl. *Ht:* 60 cm; *D:* T; *Fl:* 7–9

Bell heather

E. cinerea

Spls hrlss

Leaves hrlss in whorls of 3; infl less dense than *E. tetralix*. *Ht:* 55 cm; *D:* W; *Fl:* 7–9

Dorset heath

E. ciliaris

Stems have short hrs

Erect to 80 cm, lvs in whorls of 3, hry at edges, infl one-sided. *D:* W; *Fl:* 6–9

Cornish heath

E. vagans

Ptl tube wide, stamens protruding

Hairless; lvs in whorls of 4–5. Infl dense, each fl on long stk. *Ht:* 60 cm; *D:* W; *Fl:* 7–8

Spring heather

E. herbacea

Plant prostrate

Leaves in whorls of 4, stamens project from ptl tube. *Ht:* 15 cm; *D:* S, C; *Fl:* 3–12

Irish heath

E. erigena

Plant hrlss

Leaves in whorls of 4; fls not inflated, stamens just project. *Ht:* to 2 m; *D:* SW; *Fl:* 3–5

St Dabeoc's heath

Daboecia cantabrica

Lvs to 1 cm

Stems hry, lvs white below. Infl 3–10 fls, 4 hry spls. *Ht:* 35 cm; *D:* W; *Fl:* 7–9

Bilberry

Vaccinium myrtillus

Lvs serrate

Fr 8 mm

Deciduous, stems green, v ridged; berry black with bloom. *Ht:* 45 cm; *D:* T; *Fl:* 4–6

Cowberry

V. vitis-idaea

Lvs dull below

Evergreen, lvs round, glossy above; fl 6 mm, bell-shaped. *Ht:* 20 cm; *D:* N, C; *Fl:* 6–8

Cranberry

V. oxycoccos

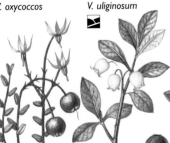

Creeps to 80 cm; shs slender, lvs oval. Ptl tube cut almost to base. *D:* N, C; *Fl:* 6–8

Bog whortleberry

V. uliginosum

Stems round, lvs untoothed, decid; fr has bloom. *Ht:* 40 cm; *D:* N, C; *Fl:* 5–6

Alpine bearberry

Arctostaphylos uva-ursi

Lvs blunt

Prostrate evergreen to 2 m. Infl 5–12 fls; fr to 8 mm, red, tastes dry. *D:* T; *Fl:* 5–7

Black bearberry

A. alpinus

Prostrate, decid to 2 m; serrate lvs strongly veined; fr juicy, black to 1 cm. *D:* S mts, N; *Fl:* 5–8

Wild azalea

Loiseleuria procumbens

Fl has 5 stamens

Prostrate, evergreen to 30 cm. Lvs numerous, opp to 8 mm; ptls have spreading lobes. *D:* T; *Fl:* 5–7

Mountain heather	Leatherleaf	Bog rosemary
Phyllodoce caerulea	*Chamaedaphne calyculata*	*Andromeda polifolia*

Fl 6 mm

Erect evergreen; lvs dense, fls to 8 mm, long-stkd, 5 stamens in terminal infl. *Ht:* 10 cm; *D:* N; *Fl:* 6–7

Erect evergreen; lvs slightly serrate, scaly below to 4 cm; infl 5–20 drooping fls. *Ht:* 35 cm; *D:* NE; *Fl:* 6–7

Creeping evergreen to 30 cm. Lvs elongate to 3.5 cm, darker above; fls long-stkd, infl 2–8 fls. *D:* T; *Fl:* 5–6

Ledum	Rhododendron
Ledum palustre	*Rhododendron ponticum*

Lvs to 4.5 cm

Many rust-coloured hrs on stems and lf undersides; fls long-stkd, infl dense. *Ht:* 80 cm, *D:* N, C; *Fl:* 6–7

Evergreen to 3 m; lvs hrlss, paler below. Infl dense, fls open, bell shaped, 10 stamens. *D:* W; *Fl:* 5–6

Crowberry family Empetraceae

Heath-like dwarf evergreens with 6 sepal and petal lobes that are not brightly coloured, and three stamens.

Crowberry

Empetrum nigrum

Fl to 2 mm diam
Fr 5 mm

Prostrate evergreen to 30 cm, stems red. Lvs linear, white line below; fls in lf axils in gps of 1–3; fr round, black. *D:* S mts, N; *Fl:* 5–6

Primrose family Primulaceae

Simple-leaved herbs. Symmetrical tubular flowers have parts in fives and stamens joined to the petal tube interior.

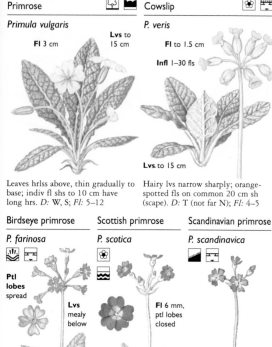

Primrose

Primula vulgaris

Lvs to 15 cm

Fl 3 cm

Leaves hrlss above, thin gradually to base; indiv fl shs to 10 cm have long hrs. *D:* W, S; *Fl:* 5–12

Cowslip

P. veris

Fl to 1.5 cm

Infl 1–30 fls

Lvs to 15 cm

Hairy lvs narrow sharply; orange-spotted fls on common 20 cm sh (scape). *D:* T (not far N); *Fl:* 4–5

Birdseye primrose

P. farinosa

Ptl lobes spread

Lvs mealy below

White lvs have crinkly edges; fr longer than spl tube, scape 10 cm. *D:* mts T; *Fl:* 5–6

Scottish primrose

P. scotica

Fl 6 mm, ptl lobes closed

As *P. farinosa* but lvs uncrinkled, fr almost equals spl tube, scape 6 cm. *D:* Scot; *Fl:* 5–9

Scandinavian primrose

P. scandinavica

Like *P. scotica* but scape to 10 cm, fl to 1 cm, longer bracts. *D:* Scand mts; *Fl:* 6–9

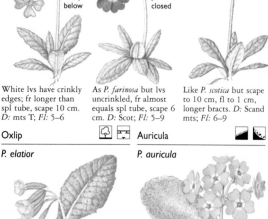

Oxlip

P. elatior

Lvs to 20 cm

Fl to 1.8 cm

Leaves as *P. veris* but hrs curled; scape to 30 cm, hry; spl tube has dark ridges. *D:* S, W, C; *Fl:* 4–5

Auricula

P. auricula

Broad lvs hrlss, succ, thick at edges; scape to 16 cm, infl to 30 fls. *D:* Alps, Carp; *Fl:* 5–7

Cyclamen   ## Sowbread   ## Alpine snowbell

Cyclamen purpurascens

C. hederifolium

Soldanella alpina

Fl to 3 cm

Lf to 8 cm

Tuberous base to 3 cm, ptl lobes clawless below, fl sh to 15 cm. D: C, S; Fl: 6–10

Corm to 15 cm; lvs to 14 cm, angled edges. Ptl lobes to 2 cm, clawed at base; fl sh to 30 cm, coiled fr stk. D: S; Fl: 8–11

Round, long-stkd lvs to 4 cm wide. Fl to 1.3 cm, many narrow lobes, fl sh to 15 cm. D: S, C; Fl: 4–7

Chickweed wintergreen

Trientalis europaea

Fl to 1.8 cm

Lvs rigid, pointed, unstkd

Erect, hrlss stems to 25 cm not branched; 1 or 2 fls on stks to 7 cm from lf whorl. D: S mts, N; Fl: 6–7

Large androsace

Androsace maxima

Fl 6 mm

Lvs 3 cm

Annual; 1 to sev 8 cm scapes, bracts large, lfy; spls longer than ptls. D: S, C; Fl: 4–5

White androsace

A. lactea

Fl stks long

Tufted per; lvs linear sessile; sev scapes to 15 cm. Stolons present. D: S, C; Fl: 6–8

Scarlet pimpernel

Anagallis arvensis

Prostrate, stems square; lvs opp, spots below. Fl stks slim, globular fr. Ht: 20 cm; D: T; Fl: 6–8

Bog pimpernel

A. tenella

Fl 1 cm

Stems round; lvs opp, shorter than slim fl shs. Ptl tube longer than spls. Ht: 10 cm; D: W; Fl: 6–8

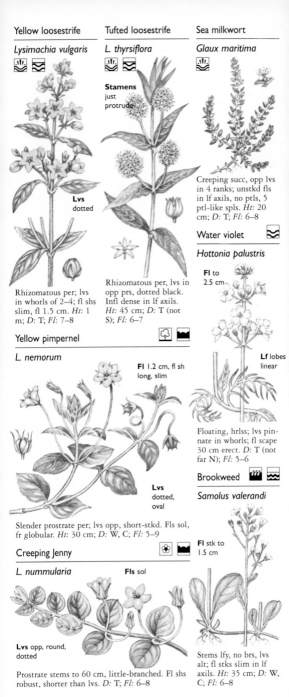

Yellow loosestrife

Lysimachia vulgaris

Rhizomatous per; lvs in whorls of 2–4; fl shs slim, fl 1.5 cm. *Ht:* 1 m; *D:* T; *Fl:* 7–8

Lvs dotted

Tufted loosestrife

L. thyrsiflora

Stamens just protrude

Rhizomatous per, lvs in opp prs, dotted black. Infl dense in lf axils. *Ht:* 45 cm; *D:* T (not S); *Fl:* 6–7

Sea milkwort

Glaux maritima

Creeping succ, opp lvs in 4 ranks; unstkd fls in lf axils, no ptls, 5 ptl-like spls. *Ht:* 20 cm; *D:* T; *Fl:* 6–8

Water violet

Hottonia palustris

Fl to 2.5 cm

Lf lobes linear

Floating, hrlss; lvs pinnate in whorls; fl scape 30 cm erect. *D:* T (not far N); *Fl:* 5–6

Yellow pimpernel

L. nemorum

Fl 1.2 cm, fl sh long, slim

Lvs dotted, oval

Slender prostrate per; lvs opp, short-stkd. Fls sol, fr globular. *Ht:* 30 cm; *D:* W, C; *Fl:* 5–9

Brookweed

Samolus valerandi

Fl stk to 1.5 cm

Stems lfy, no brs, lvs alt; fl stks slim in lf axils. *Ht:* 35 cm; *D:* W, C; *Fl:* 6–8

Creeping Jenny

L. nummularia

Fls sol

Lvs opp, round, dotted

Prostrate stems to 60 cm, little-branched. Fl shs robust, shorter than lvs. *D:* T; *Fl:* 6–8

Sea-lavender family Plumbaginaceae

Simple-leaved perennials. Clustered flowers have parts in fives, with sepals in a tube and petals just joined below.

Thrift	Jersey thrift

Armeria maritima

Dense basal lf rosette, lvs narrow, 1-veined. Scape to 30 cm, short-stkd 8 mm fls, lobes of spl tube sharply pointed. *D:* T; *Fl:* 4–10

A. arenaria

Lvs broad

As *A. maritima* but scape to 60 cm; lvs 3–5 veined; points on spl tube long, hr-like. *D:* SW; *Fl:* 6–9

Sea-lavender	Rock sea-lavender

Limonium vulgare

Lvs to 12 cm

Leaves succ, veins pinnate; scape to 30 cm, many fls on short stks, infl branched. *D:* S; *Fl:* 7–10

L. binervosum

Like *L. vulgare* but lvs smaller, rounder, no pinnate veins, 3 veins below. *Ht:* 20 cm; *D:* W; *Fl:* 7–9

Gentian family Gentianaceae

Hairless herbs with simple stalkless opposite leaves and tubular 4–5 lobed flowers. The stamens join the petals.

Marsh gentian

Gentiana pneumonanthe

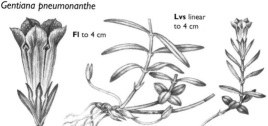

Fl to 4 cm

Lvs linear to 4 cm

Erect per to 40 cm. Terminal infl 1–7 fls, spl lobes joined by membrane as in all *Gentiana* spp, ptl lobes 3-veined. *D:* T (not far N); *Fl:* 8–9

Spring gentian

Gentiana verna

Ptl tube 2 cm long

Perennial; lvs to 1.5 cm in rosettes make a compact cushion. Fls sol, terminal, spl tube ridged. *Ht:* 4 cm; *D:* C, *Fl:* 4–6

Great yellow gentian

G. lutea

Robust, uprt per to 1.2 m. Fls crowded in lf axils and at apex, ptl tube has 5–9 lobes, longer than tube. *D:* C, S mts; *Fl:* 6–8

Alpine gentian

G. nivalis

Lvs to 5 mm

Delicate, uprt ann; fls sol, ptl tube to 1.5 cm. *Ht:* to 15 cm; *D:* N, S; *Fl:* 7–9

Purple gentian

G. purpurea   **Spl tube** split

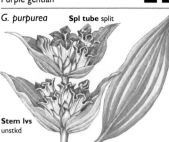

Stem lvs unstkd

Erect per to 30 cm. Fls clustered at apex and in lf axils, ptls spotted. *D:* C; *Fl:* 7–8

Cross gentian

G. cruciata

Stem lvs many, unstkd

Flowers in terminal gps, ptl tube 2 cm, 4-lobed. *Ht:* 35 cm; *D:* S, C, E; *Fl:* 6–9

Slender gentian

Gentianella tenella

Flowers much shorter than fl shs, spl tube deeply cut. *Ht:* 7 cm; *D:* T (not UK); *Fl:* 7–8

Autumn gentian

G. amarella

Fls unstkd

Sepal tube cut to under ¾ of length, 4 or 5 equal spl lobes. *Ht:* 20 cm; *D:* N, C; *Fl:* 7–10

Field gentian

Gentianella campestris

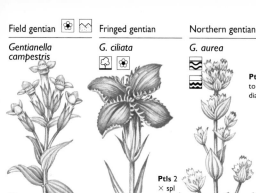

Plant erect

Flower parts in 4s, 2 outer lobes of spl tube much longer than other 2. *Ht:* 20 cm; *D:* N, C; *Fl:* 7–10

Fringed gentian

G. ciliata

Flowers sol or in loose clusters; 4 ptl lobes, fringed at edges. *Ht:* 17 cm; *D:* T (not N, W); *Fl:* 8–10

Ptls 2 × spl tube

Northern gentian

G. aurea

Ptl lobes to 1 cm diam

Flowers in dense terminal gps, 4 or 5 ptl lobes. *Ht:* 10 cm; *D:* Arct; *Fl:* 7–8

Common centaury

Centaurium erythraea

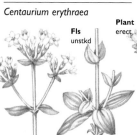

Fls unstkd

Rounded oval lvs to 5 cm long, 2 cm diam in basal rosette. *Ht:* 30 cm; *D:* T (not far N); *Fl:* 6–10

Seaside centaury

C. littorale

Plant erect

Infl dense

Leaves in basal rosette 2 cm long, under 5 mm diam, fls unstkd. *Ht:* 15 cm; *D:* NW, EC; *Fl:* 7–8

Yellow wort

Blackstonia perfoliata

Glaucous ann; fls to 1.5 cm, 6–8 ptl and spl lobes. *Ht:* 30 cm; *D:* W, C, S; *Fl:* 6–10

Marsh felwort

Swertia perennis

Fl 3 cm diam

Petal and spl tubes 4–5 lobed, cut nearly to base. *Ht:* 45 cm; *D:* mts T (not UK); *Fl:* 7–9

Yellow centaury

Cicendia filiformis

Delicate ann, long-stkd fls to 5 mm, 4 ptl lobes. Lvs to 6 mm. *Ht:* 8 cm; *D:* W, S; *Fl:* 6–10

Bogbean family Menyanthaceae

Alternate-leaved aquatics. The 5 petals and sepals are in deep-lobed tubes; the stamens join the petal tube.

Bogbean	Fringed water lily
Menyanthes trifoliata	*Nymphoides peltata*

Fl stks *c.* 1 cm

Fl stks to 7 cm

Flower stks and 3-lobed lvs above water. Ptl tube 1.5 cm, fringed edges. *Ht:* 20 cm; *D:* T; *Fl:* 5–7

Leaves 8 cm, v notched at base. Fls 3 cm, long-stkd, fringed ptl lobes. *D:* T (not far N); *Fl:* 7–8

Periwinkle family Apocynaceae

Woody plants with symmetrical 5-part flowers. The petal lobes twist in bud and the stamens join the petal tube.

Lesser periwinkle   Greater periwinkle

Vinca minor   *V. major*

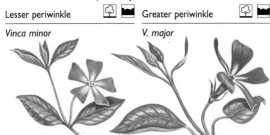

Creeps to 60 cm. Lvs v short-stkd, hrlss; fls sol to 3 cm, spl tube hrlss. *D:* S, W, C; *Fl:* 3–5

Scrambles to 1 m. Lf stks to 1 cm, fl shs uprt, fls to 5 cm, spl lobes hry at edge. *D:* W, C; *Fl:* 4–6

Milkweed family Asclepiadaceae

Perennials, often with milky sap. Tubular flowers have parts in fives; stamens fused in a ring join the stigma.

Vincetoxicum

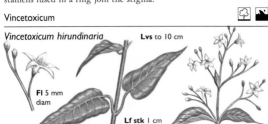

Vincetoxicum hirundinaria   **Lvs** to 10 cm

Fl 5 mm diam

Lf stk 1 cm

Perennial herb to 1.2 m. Lvs broadly oval. Infl both axillary and terminal has 6–10 fls on long stks. *D:* T (not UK); *Fl:* 6–9

Bedstraw family Rubiaceae

Herbs or woody plants with unlobed, small whorled leaves. Small densely grouped flowers have parts in fours or fives, tiny or no sepals, petals in a tube and inferior ovaries.

Wild madder

Rubia peregrina

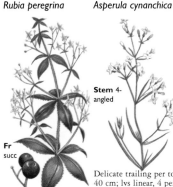

Fr succ

Robust evergreen, stem 4-angled, down-pointed prickles; lvs leathery, prickly. *Ht:* 1 m; *D:* S, W; *Fl:* 6–8

Woodruff

Galium odoratum

Lvs 6 per whorl

Creeping per, rhizomatous; erect shs to 45 cm. Forward-pointing prickles. Long ptl tube equals ptl lobes. *D:* T; *Fl:* 5–6

Fen bedstraw

G. uliginosum

Clambering stems rough to touch. Whorls 6–8 lvs, sharp point. Infl narrow in lf axis. *Ht:* 60 cm; *D:* W; *Fl:* 7–8

Squinancywort

Asperula cynanchica

Stem 4-angled

Delicate trailing per to 40 cm; lvs linear, 4 per whorl, fls 6 mm. *D:* T; *Fl:* 6–8

Hedge bedstraw

G. mollugo

Lvs broad, 6–8 whorl

Stout per to 1.2 m. Prickles at lf edge point forwards. Infl large, dense. *D:* T; *Fl:* 6–9

Lady's bedstraw

G. verum

Mat-forming, erect shs to 1 m, lvs fine, 2 cm, 8–12 per whorl, fls 3 mm. *D:* T; *Fl:* 7–8

Blue woodruff

A. arvensis

Plant uprt

Leaves 6–9 per whorl; fls 4 mm, hry bracts longer than fls. *Ht:* 20 cm; *D:* T; *Fl:* 4–6

Heath bedstraw

G. saxatile

Prostrate with fl shs to 20 cm. Prickles at lf edges point forwards. *D:* W, C; *Fl:* 6–8

Crosswort

Cruciata laevipes

Fls in lf axils

Stems hry

Scrambles to 70 cm. Lvs 4 per whorl, hry, broad, 3-veined. *D:* W, S, C; *Fl:* 5–6

Slender bedstraw

Galium pumilum

Infl loose, terminal

Low shs to 30 cm, few prickles pointing backwards; fls long-stkd. *D:* W, C; *Fl:* 6–7

Common cleavers

G. aparine

Fl 2 mm

Very prickly; fls on axillary stks have whorls of bracts. *Ht:* 1 m; *D:* T; *Fl:* 6–8

False cleavers

G. spurium

As *G. aparine* but fls 1 mm, only 2 bracts on fl stk, lvs narrow. *Ht:* 1 m; *D:* T; *Fl:* 7

Field madder

Sherardia arvensis

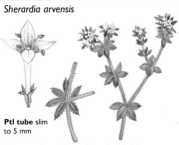

Ptl tube slim to 5 mm

Prostrate shs to 40 cm. Terminal infl has many bracts, spls evident, esp in fr. *D:* T; *Fl:* 5–10

Northern bedstraw

G. boreale

Lvs to 4 cm

Erect, stiff shs to 45 cm. Lvs 3-veined, 4 per whorl; loose infl. *D:* T; *Fl:* 7–8

Marsh bedstraw

G. palustre

Lvs 4–6 per whorl

Delicate, scrambling to 1.2 m. Lvs blunt-tipped; infl spread, loose, v branched. *D:* T; *Fl:* 7

Jacob's-ladder family Polemoniaceae

Symmetrical-flowered herbs. The 5-lobed sepal and petal tubes and 5 stamens lie above the 3-stigma ovary.

Jacob's-ladder

Polemonium caeruleum

Lvs to 40 cm

Erect lfy shs from rhizome. Lvs pinnate, 6–12 lflt prs. Fls to 3 cm diam, v short ptl tube, stamens fill fl mouth. *Ht:* 60 cm; *D:* N, C; *Fl:* 6–7

Convolvulus family Convolvulaceae

Climbers with a milky sap. Flowers have 5 petals in a funnel and 5 free sepals. The stamens join the petal tube.

Field bindweed	Common dodder	Greater dodder
Convolvulus arvensis	*Cuscuta epithymum*	*C. europaea*

Climbs anticlockwise to 75 cm. Fls 2 cm, fl stk has 2 bracts well below spls. Lvs 4 cm. *D:* T; *Fl:* 6–9

Parasite on heather, gorse; lvs are scales, shs red; styles longer than ovary. *Ht:* 1 m; *D:* T (not far N); *Fl:* 7–9

Parasite on hops and nettles. Stems robust, styles shorter than ovary. *Ht:* 1 m; *D:* T (not far N); *Fl:* 8–9

Hedge bindweed	Sea bindweed	Great bindweed
Calystegia sepium	*C. soldanella*	*C. silvatica*

Lvs to 15 cm

Fl to 5 cm

Climber. Fls 6 cm, swollen bracts longer than and enclosing spls. *Ht:* 2 m; *D:* T (not far N); *Fl:* 7–9

Prostrate shs to 60 cm. Lvs 3 cm, long-stkd, kidney-shaped; bracts smaller than spls. *D:* W *Fl:* 6–8

Strong, hrlss, clambering stems. Bracts wide and overlapping (not in *C. sepium*). *Ht:* 3 m; *D:* W & S; *Fl:* 7–9

Borage family Boraginaceae

Coarse-haired herbs. The coiled inflorescence has the oldest flowers below. Tubular pink or blue flowers have 5 joined petals and sepals, one style and a 4-lobed ovary.

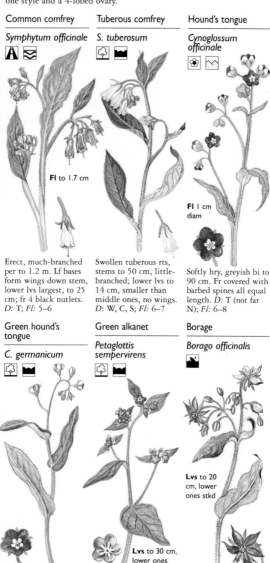

Common comfrey

Symphytum officinale

Fl to 1.7 cm

Erect, much-branched per to 1.2 m. Lf bases form wings down stem, lower lvs largest, to 25 cm; fr 4 black nutlets. *D:* T; *Fl:* 5–6

Tuberous comfrey

S. tuberosum

Swollen tuberous rts, stems to 50 cm, little-branched; lower lvs to 14 cm, smaller than middle ones, no wings. *D:* W, C, S; *Fl:* 6–7

Hound's tongue

Cynoglossum officinale

Fl 1 cm diam

Softly hry, greyish bi to 90 cm. Fr covered with barbed spines all equal length. *D:* T (not far N); *Fl:* 6–8

Green hound's tongue

C. germanicum

Like *C. officinale* but greener, hrs rougher; lvs near-hrlss above, outer fr spines longer than inner. *Ht:* 60 cm; *D:* W, C; *Fl:* 5–7

Green alkanet

Petaglottis sempervirens

Lvs to 30 cm, lower ones stkd

Coarse-hrd per to 1 m. Long-stkd infls in lf axils. Fl 1 cm has white scales in mouth of ptl tube. *D:* SW; *Fl:* 5–6

Borage

Borago officinalis

Lvs to 20 cm, lower ones stkd

Robust ann to 60 cm. Fls 2 cm diam on long stks to 4 cm; stamens protruding, purple. *D:* C, S; *Fl:* 6–8

Nonea Common gromwell

Nonea pulla

Lithospermum officinale

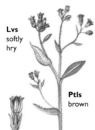

Lvs softly hry

Ptls brown

Ptls to 4 mm diam

Plant roughly hry

Much-branched per to 80 cm. Lvs have obvious side nerves. Nuts white, glossy. *D:* T; *Fl:* 6–7

Erect ann or per to 50 cm. Fls to 1.5 cm, ptl tube 2 × spls. *D:* E, EC; *Fl:* 4–5

Alkanet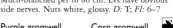

Anchusa officinalis

Lvs to 12 cm

Fl 1 cm diam

Erect v branched per to 80 cm. Infl dense, stms not protruding. *D:* C, S; *Fl:* 6–8

Purple gromwell

Lithospermum purpurocaeruleum

Creeping per, uprt fl shs to 60 cm. Ptls 1.5 cm, 2 × spl length. *D:* S, C; *Fl:* 5–6

Corn gromwell

L. arvensis

Fl to 4 mm diam

Stems little branched

Erect ann to 50 cm. Lvs have no obvious side veins; nut brown, warty. *D:* T; *Fl:* 5–7

Bugloss

Buglossoides arvensis

Lvs to 10 cm

Bristly uprt ann to 60 cm. Lvs wavy at edges; ptl tube just curved. *D:* T; *Fl:* 5–9

Lungwort

Pulmonaria officinalis

Lf stks winged

Short-hrd per to 30 cm. Fl 1 cm, tufts of hrs alternate with stamens. *D:* C, S, W; *Fl:* 3–5

Tufted forget-me-not

Myosotis laxa

Has flattened hrs on lvs, spls and rounded stems. Fl 4 mm. *Ht:* 30 cm; *D:* T; *Fl:* 5–8

Wood forget-me-not

M. sylvatica

Erect per to 45 cm, spread hrs on lvs and stems, curled hrs on spls. Fr stks 2 × spls. *D:* T (not N); *Fl:* 5–9

Early forget-me-not

M. ramosissima

Fl 2 mm

Delicate, has spread hrs. *M. discolor* sim, but fls yellow. *Ht:* 25 cm; *D:* T (not N); *Fl:* 4–6

Field forget-me-not

M. arvensis

Plant uprt

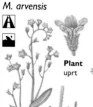

Spread hrs on lvs and spls. Fr stks 2 × spl length; fls 5 mm. *Ht:* 20 cm; *D:* T; *Fl:* 4–9

Creeping forget-me-not

M. secunda

Hairs on stem spread, on spls flat. Fr stks 3–5 × spl length. *Ht:* 45 cm; *D:* W; *Fl:* 5–8

Marsh forget-me-not

M. scorpioides

Flat hrs on lvs and spls. Stems ridged; fr stks 2 × spls. *Ht:* 30 cm; *D:* C, N; *Fl:* 5–9

Bur forget-me-not

Lappula squarrosa

Lvs to 7 cm, unstkd

Delicate bristly ann, erect shs to 70 cm. Fr has 2 rows of hooked spines. *D:* T (not NW); *Fl:* 6–7

Madwort

Asperugo procumbens

Lvs to 7 cm

Coarsely hry, trailing ann. Spls enlarge into 2-lipped fr covering. *Ht:* 45 cm; *D:* N, C, E; *Fl:* 5–7

Oyster plant	Navelwort	Viper's bugloss
Mertensia maritima	*Omphalodes scorpioides*	*Echium vulgare*

Fl 6 mm

Lvs to 4 cm

Lvs in 2 rows

Lvs have strong centre veins

Straggling, hrlss, succ per to 60 cm, fl stks to 1 cm, stamens just protruding. *D:* NW; *Fl:* 6–8

Straggles to 40 cm. Fls to 4 mm sol in lf axils, obvious lobes at ptl tube mouth. *D:* C, E; *Fl:* 4–5

Roughly hry. Ptl tube lobes unequal, 4 protruding stamens. *Ht:* 65 cm; *D:* T; *Fl:* 6–9

Vervain family Verbenaceae

Plants whose flowers have 5 sepals in a tube, 5 petals (often in a two-lipped tube),and usually 4 stamens.

Vervain

Verbena officinalis

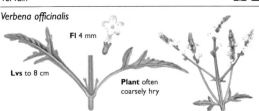

Fl 4 mm

Lvs to 8 cm

Plant often coarsely hry

Stiff, erect, woody per. Lvs pinnate, lobed. Infl a delicate spike at apex, spl tube ribbed. Fr 4 nutlets. *Ht:* 45 cm; *D:* T (not N); *Fl:* 7–9

Water-starwort family Callitrichaceae

Slender aquatics with simple leaves. Separate male and female flowers on the same plant have no sepals or petals.

Water-starwort

Callitriche stagnalis

♀ **fl** has 2 styles

Submerged lvs narrow, floating lvs spathulate in rosette. Stems to 60 cm, fr 2 mm, strongly keeled. ♂ fl has 1 stamen. *D:* T; *Fl:* 5–9

Mint family Lamiaceae

Square-stemmed herbs with opposite leaves. Flowers in axillary whorls have 2-lipped petal and sepal tubes (the sepal tube 5-lobed, the petal tube three-lobed below) and 4 stamens.

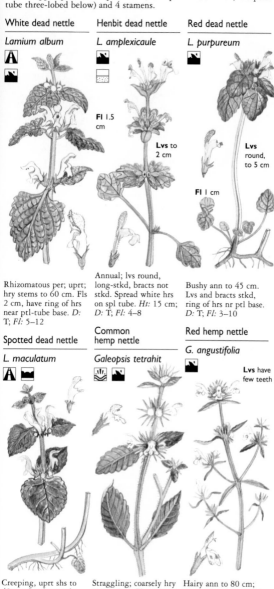

White dead nettle

Lamium album

Rhizomatous per; uprt; hry stems to 60 cm. Fls 2 cm, have ring of hrs near ptl-tube base. *D:* T; *Fl:* 5–12

Henbit dead nettle

L. amplexicaule

Fl 1.5 cm

Lvs to 2 cm

Annual; lvs round, long-stkd, bracts not stkd. Spread white hrs on spl tube. *Ht:* 15 cm; *D:* T; *Fl:* 4–8

Red dead nettle

L. purpureum

Lvs round, to 5 cm

Fl 1 cm

Bushy ann to 45 cm. Lvs and bracts stkd, ring of hrs nr ptl base. *D:* T; *Fl:* 3–10

Spotted dead nettle

L. maculatum

Creeping, uprt shs to 40 cm. Lvs have pale patch; fls 2 cm, ring of hrs in ptl tube. *D:* S, C; *Fl:* 5–10

Common hemp nettle

Galeopsis tetrahit

Straggling; coarsely hry ann to 1 m. Fls to 2 cm, white, pink or purple; ptls often spotted. *D:* T; *Fl:* 7–9

Red hemp nettle

G. angustifolia

Lvs have few teeth

Hairy ann to 80 cm; narrow lvs to 8 cm. Fls to 2.5 cm, ptl tube far longer than spls. *D:* W, S, C; *Fl:* 7–10

Large-flowered hemp nettle

G. speciosa

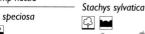

Flowers to 3 cm; vary in col but always have some yellow; ptl tube 2 × spls. *Ht:* 1 m; *D:* T; *Fl:* 7–9

Downy woundwort

S. germanica

Dense, long white hrs give a greyish look. Lvs narrow, blades to 1.2 cm; fls in dense whorls. *Ht:* 60 cm; *D:* S, W, C; *Fl:* 7–8

Hedge woundwort

Stachys sylvatica

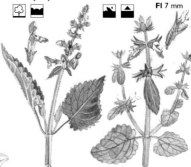

Green rhizomes; uprt shs to 1 m. Lvs 9 cm; oval, all stkd; fls 1.4 cm. *D:* T; *Fl:* 7–8

Field woundwort

S. arvensis

Fl 7 mm

Delicate, branched, hry ann. Fl whorls spaced. *Ht:* 20 cm; *D:* S, W, C; *Fl:* 4–11

Marsh woundwort

S. palustris

Has rhizome. Lvs to 1.2 cm, lf stks v short; fls 1.5 cm. *Ht:* 80 cm; *D:* T; *Fl:* 7–9

Yellow woundwort

S. recta

Fl to 2 cm

Sweetly aromatic per to 1 m. Fls large in long, slim spikes. V variable. *D:* S, C; *Fl:* 6–9

Bugle	Blue bugle	Ground pine

Ajuga reptans

A. genevensis

A. chamaepitys

Has stolons; lvs in basal rosette hry on opp faces; top ptl lip short. *Ht:* 20 cm; *D:* T (not far N); *Fl:* 5–7

Erect shs to 30 cm. Lf blades hry, long-stkd; fls appear after basal lvs have died. *D:* T (not N); *Fl:* 5–7

Aromatic; hry ann; lvs cut into 3 narrow lobes. Paired fls shorter than lvs. *Ht:* 10 cm; *D:* T (not N); *Fl:* 5–9

Motherwort	Gypsywort

Leonurus cardiaca

Lycopus europaeus

Lf blades to 1.2 cm

Leaf blades palmately 5–7-lobed. Ptl tube shorter than spls. *Ht:* 1 m; *D:* T (not far N); *Fl:* 7–9

Leaves elliptical, deeply toothed. Fls 3 mm, dense whorls, only 2 stms. *Ht:* 80 cm; *D:* T; *Fl:* 6–9

Watermint	Cornmint

Mentha aquatica

M. arvensis

Smells of mint. Infl dense, terminal; ptl tube 4 equal lobes. *Ht:* 70 cm; *D:* T (not far N); *Fl:* 7–10

No strong smell. Fls in dense whorls in axils of bracts, spl tube hry. *Ht:* 45 cm; *D:* T; *Fl:* 5–10

Spearmint Catmint Common calamint

M. spicata

Nepeta cataria

Calamintha sylvatica

Fl to
2.2 cm

Strong-smelling per to
90 cm. Stem hrlss,
branched; lvs unstkd
to 9 cm. Fl whorls in
dense spike, spl tube
hrlss. *D:* T; *Fl:* 8–9

Strong-smelling herb
to 1 m. Inflorescence
dense, terminal; ptl
tube bent halfway
down. *D:* S, E; *Fl:* 7–9

Has creeping rhizome.
Uprt shs to 60 cm, lvs
round, serrate; fls stkd
in loose clusters in lf
axils. *D:* S, W; *Fl:* 8–9

Marjoram Wild thyme

Origanum vulgare

Thymus serpyllum

Lvs to
4 cm

Plant woody,
aromatic

Aromatic. Stems uprt,
branched; fls
7 mm in dense head, protruding
stamens. *Ht:* 60 cm; *D:* T; *Fl:* 7–9

Flower stks round, evenly spaced
hrs. Spl tube 2-lipped, top lip 3-
lobed. *Ht:* 20 cm; *D:* N; *Fl:* 7–8

Large wild thyme Wild thyme

T. pulegioides

T. polytrichus

Like *T. serpyllum* but stems square,
hry; at angles. Infl long. *Ht:* 20 cm;
D: T; *Fl:* 7–8

As *T. serpyllum* but stems square,
hry on opp faces. Infl short. *Ht:*
10 cm; *D:* S, W, C; *Fl:* 5–8

113

Wild basil

Clinopodium vulgare

Hairy per. Lvs just toothed; fls in dense terminal and axillary whorls. *Ht:* 60 cm; *D:* T; *Fl:* 7–9

Basil thyme

C. arvensis **Fl** to I cm

Lvs to 1.5 cm

Branched; hry ann; straggles to 20 cm. Fls in axillary whorls of 3–8. *D:* T (not far N); *Fl:* 5–9

Meadow clary

Salvia pratensis

Lvs to 15 cm

Aromatic per to 1 m; hooded fls to 2.5 cm. 2 stamens, long style. *D:* T (not N); *Fl:* 6–7

Wild sage

Teucrium scorodonia

Stem **lvs** unstkd

Stems to 60 cm have flat hrs; fl bracts longer than spl tube. *D:* C, S, E; *Fl:* 6–8

Wild clary

Salvia verbenaca

Fl to 1.5 cm

Basal lvs broad; fls have 2 white spots on lower lip. *Ht:* 60 cm; *D:* S, W; *Fl:* 5–8

Wood sage

Teucrium scorodonia

Fl 1.3 cm

Flowers in whorled terminal spike, no upper lip as all *Teucrium* spp. *Ht:* 20 cm; *D:* S, W, C; *Fl:* 7–9

Mountain germander

T. montanum

Lvs to 3 cm, hry below

Patch-forming shrub; prostrate stems 25 cm. Fls in terminal gp, bracts lf-like. *D:* C, S; *Fl:* 5–8

Wall germander	Water germander	Cut-leaved germander
T. chamaedrys	T. scordium	T. botrys

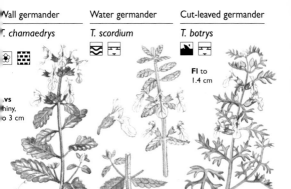

Lvs shiny, to 3 cm

Fl to 1.4 cm

| Tufted per to 30 cm. Lvs scalloped, fls in axils of lfy bracts. *D:* S, C; *Fl:* 7–9 | Serrate, unstkd lvs. Fls in axils of lfy bracts. *Ht:* 45 cm; *D:* T (not N); *Fl:* 7–10 | Leaves and bracts pinnately lobed, segs narrow. *Ht:* to 30 cm; *D:* S, W, C; *Fl:* 7–9 |

Skull cap	Lesser skull cap
Scutellaria galericulata	S. minor

Fl to 2 cm

Lvs to 5 cm

| Hairy per to 50 cm. Lvs indented at edges. Fls in bract axils, infl 1-sided. *D:* T; *Fl:* 6–9 | Like *S. galericulata* but to 15 cm. Lvs unlobed to 3 cm; fls to 1 cm, spotted. *D:* W; *Fl:* 7–10 |

Dracocephalum	Black horehound
Dracocephalum ruyschiana	Ballota nigra

Lvs to 7 cm

Stems v branched

| Near-hrlss per. Lvs linear; fls in dense spike with linear bracts. *Ht:* 50 cm; *D:* N, C; *Fl:* 7–8 | Fetid per to 1 m. Lvs to 4 cm; fls in dense whorls with big bracts, spl teeth bristly. *D:* T (not N); *Fl:* 6–10 |

115

White horehound

Marrubium vulgare

Woolly, v branched per. Lf blades blunt-toothed to 4 cm; many fls in whorls. *D:* T (not N); *Fl:* 6–11

Bastard balm

Melittis melissophyllum

Lf blades to 8 cm

Aromatic; hry per to 50 cm. Fls to 4 cm, spl tube 2-lipped, lower lip 2-lobed. *D:* W, C, S; *Fl:* 5–7

Self heal

Prunella vulgaris

Lvs to 5 cm

Stems and oval lvs often purplish, spl tube 2-lipped. *Ht:* 20 cm; *D:* T; *Fl:* 6–9

Yellow archangel

Lamiastrum galeobdolon

Has stolons. Leaves serrate. Fls 2 cm, top lip hooded. *Ht:* 40 cm; *D:* T; *Fl:* 5–6

Ground ivy

Glechoma hederacea

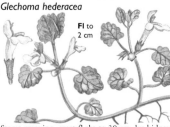

Fl to 2 cm

Stems creeping, erect fl shs to 30 cm, lvs kidney-shaped; few fls in whorl. *D:* T; *Fl:* 3–5

Cut-leaved self heal

P. laciniata

Like *P. vulgaris* but hairier leaves, deeply lobed. *Ht:* 20 cm; *D:* S, W, C; *Fl:* 6–8

Betony

Stachys officinalis

Lf stk to 7 cm

Long-stkd lvs, edges scalloped, in basal rosette. *Ht:* 45 cm; *D:* T (not far N); *Fl:* 6–9

Nightshade family Solanaceae

Alternate-leaved herbs and shrubs. Tubular symmetrical flowers are 5-lobed with stamens joining the petal tube.

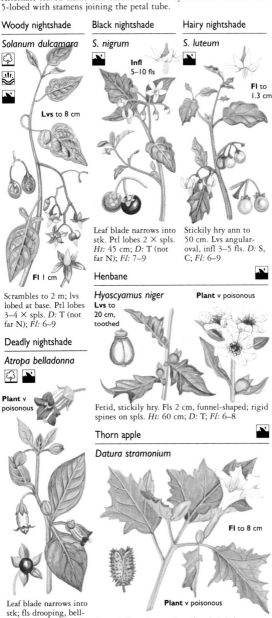

Woody nightshade

Solanum dulcamara

Lvs to 8 cm

Fl I cm

Scrambles to 2 m; lvs lobed at base. Ptl lobes 3–4 × spls. *D:* T (not far N); *Fl:* 6–9

Deadly nightshade

Atropa belladonna

Plant v poisonous

Leaf blade narrows into stk; fls drooping, bell-shaped. *Ht:* 1 m; *D:* S, W, C; *Fl:* 6–8

Black nightshade

S. nigrum

Infl 5–10 fls

Leaf blade narrows into stk. Ptl lobes 2 × spls. *Ht:* 45 cm; *D:* T (not far N); *Fl:* 7–9

Henbane

Hyoscyamus niger

Lvs to 20 cm, toothed

Plant v poisonous

Fetid, stickily hry. Fls 2 cm, funnel-shaped; rigid spines on spls. *Ht:* 60 cm; *D:* T; *Fl:* 6–8

Thorn apple

Datura stramonium

Fl to 8 cm

Plant v poisonous

Stems bifurcating, to 1 m; fls sol. Spls long, tubular; fr spiny. *D:* T (not far N); *Fl:* 7–10

Hairy nightshade

S. luteum

Fl to 1.3 cm

Stickily hry ann to 50 cm. Lvs angular-oval, infl 3–5 fls. *D:* S, C; *Fl:* 6–9

Figwort family Scrophulariaceae

Herbs, some of them partially parasitic. The 2-lipped asymmetrical flowers have 5 petals and sepals joined at least at their base, and usually 4 stamens (but sometimes 5 or 2). The ovary is 2-celled and superior, the fruit is usually a capsule.

Great mullein

Verbascum thapsus

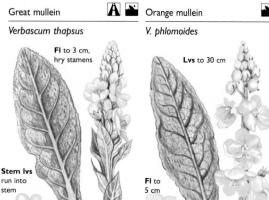

Fl to 3 cm, hry stamens

Lvs to 30 cm

Stem lvs run into stem

Fl to 5 cm

Robust bi to 2 m, dense woolly covering. Fls in tall, dense spike, 5 stamens as all *Verbascum* spp. *D:* T (not far N); *Fl:* 6–8

Orange mullein

V. phlomoides

Stem lvs do not run down stem at junction. Ptls hry on outside. *Ht:* 1 m; *D:* T (not N, UK); *Fl:* 6–8

Dark mullein

V. nigrum

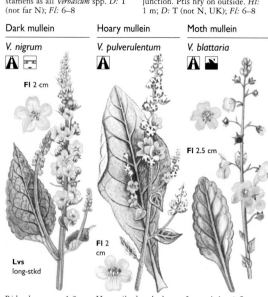

Fl 2 cm

Lvs long-stkd

Ridged stems to 1.2 m, star-shaped hrs. Hrs on stamens purple. *D:* T (not N); *Fl:* 6–10

Hoary mullein

V. pulverulentum

Fl 2 cm

Has easily detached white, woolly covering. Stamen hrs white. *Ht:* 1 m; *D:* W, S; *Fl:* 7–8

Moth mullein

V. blattaria

Fl 2.5 cm

Leaves hrlss; 1 fl per bract in infl, stamen hrs purple. *Ht:* 80 cm; *D:* S, C; *Fl:* 6–10

White mullein

Verbascum lychnitis

Ridged stems to 1.5 m; short star-shaped hrs, lvs hrlss above. *D:* S, C; *Fl:* 7–8

Germander speedwell

Veronica chamaedrys

Stems to 40 cm, rooting prostrate, with 2 lines of hrs. Infl loose from lf axils, fls 2 stamens as all *Veronica* spp. *D:* T; *Fl:* 3–7

Large speedwell

V. austriaca

Erect per to 1 m. Infl axillary, 5 spl lobes (1 may be small). *D:* T (not N); *Fl:* 6–8

Common field speedwell

V. persica

Much-branched ann to 40 cm, stems hry. Fls to 1.2 cm, sol in lf axils. Lvs to 3 cm shorter than fl stks; fr lobes diverge. *D:* T; *Fl:* 1–12

Ivy-leaved speedwell

V. hederifolia

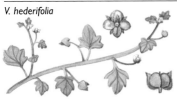

Prostrate ann, hry stems, to 60 cm. Lvs to 1.5 cm, prominent lobes. Fls sol in lf axils, stks shorter than lvs. *D:* T; *Fl:* 3–8

Heath speedwell

V. officinalis

Infl dense

Prostrate perennial, hry stems to 40 cm; infl in lf axils, 15–25 fls. *D:* T; *Fl:* 5–8

Spiked speedwell

Veronica spicata

Fl tube long

Infl a terminal spike

Hairy per to 60 cm. Lower lvs oval, top lvs linear; infl dense. *D:* T (not W); *Fl:* 7–9

Wall speedwell

V. arvensis

Erect to 25 cm. Lvs coarsely toothed; fl stks shorter than spls, top bracts longer than fls. *D:* T; *Fl:* 3–10

Spring speedwell

V. verna

Erect ann to 15 cm; lvs pinnate, 3–7 lobes; fl stks shorter than spls, fr broad. *D:* T (not far N, W); *Fl:* 5–6

Thyme-leaved speedwell

V. serpyllifolia

Prostrate per, creeps to 30 cm. Infl long, terminal, up to 30 fls. Bracts longer than fl stks. *D:* T; *Fl:* 3–10

Water speedwell

V. anagallis-aquatica

Lvs to 12 cm

Hairless per to 30 cm. Lvs long, infl in opp prs. *D:* T (not far N); *Fl:* 6–8. *V. catenata* sim but pink fls.

Rock speedwell

V. fruticans

Lvs hrlss. Infl terminal, fl stks longer than bracts. Large fl *c.* 1 cm. *Ht:* 15 cm; *D:* C mts, NW; *Fl:* 7–8

Brooklime

V. beccabunga

Hairless per to 60 cm.
Lvs round, blunt; infls
axillary in opp prs. *D:*
T (not far N); *Fl:* 5–9

Slender speedwell

V. filiformis

Mat-forming per, shs
creep to 40 cm. Lvs
kidney-shaped; fls sol,
long-stkd in fl axils.
D: NW, C; *Fl:* 4–6

Marsh speedwell

V. scutellata

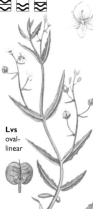

Lvs
oval-
linear

Hairless per to 50 cm;
lvs serrate to 4 cm.
Infls alt, loose in lf
axils; fl stks 2 × bracts.
D: T; *Fl:* 6–8

Eyebright

Euphrasia spp

Lvs opp

A gp of variable, semi-
parasitic anns; fls
unstkd in bract axils,
2-lipped, lower lip 3-
lobed. *Ht:* 25 cm; *D:*

Wood speedwell

V. montana

Creeping per, uprt shs
to 40 cm, hry all
round; lvs stkd. *c.*
1 cm. Infl axillary, 4–5
fls. *D:* W, C, S, *Fl:* 4–7

Fairy foxglove

Erinus alpinus

**Ptl
lobes**
spread

Tufted per to 15 cm.
Lvs alt, obovate; spl
tube narrow, 5-lobed,
ptl tube slim, 5-lobed.
D: C, S mts; *Fl:* 5–10

Foxglove	Large yellow foxglove

Digitalis purpurea

Infl
20–80 fls

Lvs to
30 cm

Stem
winged

D. grandiflora

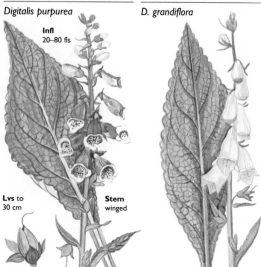

Erect bi to 1.5 m; felty hrs all over.
Fls to 5 cm spotted on lower part of
tube. *D:* W; *Fl:* 6–9

Stems uprt to 1 m; lvs fine-toothed.
Fls to 5 cm, yellow-brown network
in tube. *D:* E, C; *Fl:* 6–9

Common figwort	Water figwort	Yellow figwort
Scrophularia nodosa	*S. auriculata*	*S. vernalis*

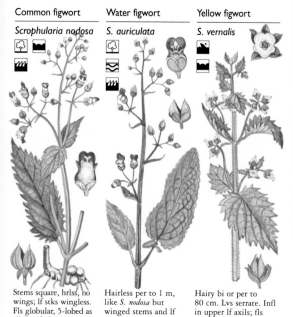

Stems square, hrlss, no
wings; lf stks wingless.
Fls globular, 5-lobed as
all *Scrophularia* spp. *Ht:*
60 cm; *D:* T; *Fl:* 6–9

Hairless per to 1 m,
like *S. nodosa* but
winged stems and lf
stks. Lvs scalloped at
edge. *D:* W; *Fl:* 6–9

Hairy bi or per to
80 cm. Lvs serrate. Infl
in upper lf axils; fls
flask-shaped, 7 mm. *D:*
S, C; *Fl:* 4–6

Balm-leaved figwort

S. scorodonia

Fl 1 cm

Grey, hry per to 1 m, stem square, no wings. Lvs serrate, oval, to 10 cm. *D:* W; *Fl:* 6–8

French figwort

S. canina

Much-branched per to 60 cm. Lvs pinnately lobed; fls to 5 mm. *D:* S, C; *Fl:* 5–8

Common toadflax

Linaria vulgaris

Fl to 2.5 cm

Stem uprt, hrlss

Flowers as *Antirrhinum* (p. 124) but with spur. *Ht:* 60 cm; *D:* T (not far N); *Fl:* 7–10

Pale toadflax

L. repens

Hairless creeping per, uprt shs, to 80 cm. Fls pale, dark-veined, spur short. *D:* S, W, C; *Fl:* 6–9

Alpine toadflax

L. alpina

Fl 2 cm

Prostrate, glaucous. Lvs in whorls; fls long-spurred, 3–15 per gp. *Ht:* 20 cm; *D:* C, E; *Fl:* 6–9

Ivy-leaved toadflax

Cymbalaria muralis

Stems hrlss, trail to 80 cm. Lvs alt, round, 5-lobed, long-stkd. Fls to 1 cm, sol in lf axils, yellow patch at mouth. *D:* S, W, C; *Fl:* 5–11

Daisy-leaved toadflax

Anarrhinum bellidifolium

Fl to 5 mm

Plant hrlss

Basal lvs to 8 cm, oval, serrate; stem lvs v cut, 3–5 narrow segs. Infl a spike. *Ht:* 60 cm; *D:* SW; *Fl:* 3–8

Leafy lousewort

P. foliosa

Leafy per to 50 cm, shs hry. Infl dense spike of yellow fls, lfy bracts longer than fls. *D:* S, C; *Fl:* 6–8

Snapdragon

Antirrhinum majus

Woody per to 80 cm, brs from base. Infl terminal; fls to 4 cm, variable colour, no spur. *D:* SW; *Fl:* 7–9

Marsh lousewort

P. palustris

Annual; 1 main uprt stem. Spls 2-lipped, hry, top ptl lip has tooth on each side. *Ht:* 45 cm; *D:* T; *Fl:* 5–9

Lousewort

Pedicularis sylvatica

Lvs to 2 cm

Perennial, trails to 25 cm. Spls hrlss, not 2-lipped, no lateral teeth on top ptl lip. *D:* W, C; *Fl:* 4–7

Moor king

P.sceptrum-carolinum

Erect per. Lvs to 2 cm, most in basal rosette, few stem lvs; infl a spike, fls 3 cm. *Ht:* 60 cm; *D:* N, C; *Fl:* 7–8

Gratiola

Gratiola officinalis

Lvs opp

Hairless per, stems hollow, 4-angled; fls long-stkd, sol in lf axils. *Ht:* to 50 cm; *D:* S, C; *Fl:* 5–10

Yellow rattle

Rhinanthus minor

Fl to 1.5 cm

Semi-parasitic per to 50 cm, lvs green, opp; spl tube flat, inflated in fr. A variable sp. *D:* T; *Fl:* 5–8

Red bartsia

Odontites vernus

Hairy, v branched ann to 50 cm. Infl dense spike; fls 1 cm, 2-lipped, no teeth on top lip. *D:* T; *Fl:* 6–8

Mudwort

Limosella aquatica

Fl to 5 mm, 4–5-lobed

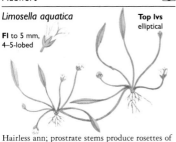

Top lvs elliptical

Hairless ann; prostrate stems produce rosettes of lvs to 1 cm. Fls sol in lf axils, spls longer than ptl tube. *D:* T (local); *Fl:* 6–10

Small toadflax

Chaenorrhinum minus

Annual with glandular hairy, erect stems. Lvs almost unstalked linear simple. Solitary fls in lf axils. *Ht:* 8–25 cm; *D:* S; *Fl:* 5–10

Yellow odontites

O. lutea

Fl to 8 mm

Erect, hrlss ann to 40 cm, many brs; infl loose. Linear bracts, fls hry, stamens protrude. *D:* S, C; *Fl:* 7–9

Sharp-leaved fluellen

Kickxia elatine

Fl stks long, hrlss

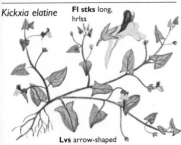

Lvs arrow-shaped

Slim, prostrate shs to 50 cm. Fls as *Linaria* (p. 123), sol, axillary. *D:* S, W, C; *Fl:* 7–10

Round-leaved fluellen

K. spuria

Like *K. elatine* but hry and more robust. Lvs round, fls 1 cm, stks hry. *D:* S, W, C; *Fl:* 7–10

Field cow-wheat

Melampyrum arvense

Top lvs toothed nr base

Hairy ann to 60 cm, lvs unstkd. Infl dense spike; bracts narrow, toothed, uprt, pink. *D:* T (not far N); *Fl:* 6–9

Crested cow-wheat

M. cristatum

Little-branched ann to 50 cm. Infl dense 4-angled spike; bracts toothed, curl back. *D:* T (rare in N); *Fl:* 6–9

Common cow-wheat

M. pratense

Leaves unstkd. Fls in axils of lfy bracts, ptls 2 × spls. *Ht:* to 60 cm; *D:* T; *Fl:* 5–10

Wood cow-wheat

M. sylvaticum

Very like *M. pratense* but spl lobes spread and about same length as ptls. *Ht:* 25 cm; *D:* S mts, N; *Fl:* 6–8

Lvs to 10 cm

Melampyrum

M. nemorosum

Hairy, uprt ann to 50 cm. Lvs oval to 4 cm wide; fls 2 cm, bracts bluish-violet, infl lfy. *D:* N, C; *Fl:* 6–8

Yellow bartsia

Parentucellia viscosa

Stem not branched

Erect, stickily hry ann to 50 cm. Lvs not lobed. Fls 2 cm, top lip shorter than lower. *D:* S, W; *Fl:* 6–10

Alpine bartsia

Bartsia alpina

Fl 2 cm

Lvs opp, unstkd, to 2 cm

Hairy per to 20 cm. Purple bracts in infl, top fl lip longer than lower. *D:* S mts, N; *Fl:* 6–8

Cornish moneywort

Sibthorpia europaea

Lvs to 2 cm

Creeps to 40 cm. Lvs rounded, 5–7-lobed; fls 2 mm, sol, short-stkd in lf axils. *D:* W; *Fl:* 7–10

Monkey flower

Mimulus guttatus

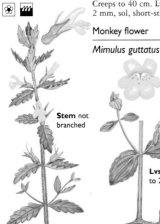

Lvs opp, unstkd, to 2 cm

Fl to 5 cm, tube broad

Perennial to 50 cm. Lvs rounded, toothed, to 7 cm. Fls sol in bract axils. *D:* T; *Fl:* 7–9

127

Globularia family Globulariaceae

Simple-leaved perennials. Flowers in very dense heads have 5 sepals and petals, 4 stamens and a one-celled ovary.

Globularia

Globularia vulgaris

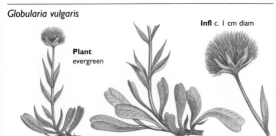

Plant evergreen

Infl c. 1 cm diam

Rosette lvs have 3 teeth at tip and narrow gradually, stem lvs unlobed, unstkd. Fls 2-lipped, lower lip 3-lobed. *Ht:* 20 cm; *D:* S, Swed; *Fl:* 4–6

Broomrape family Orobanchaceae

Parasites on plant roots and lacking green pigment. Leaves are scales, flowers two-lipped with a bent petal tube.

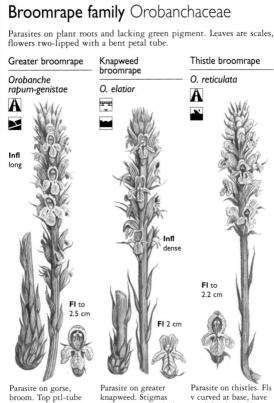

Greater broomrape	Knapweed broomrape	Thistle broomrape
Orobanche rapum-genistae	*O. elatior*	*O. reticulata*

Infl long

Infl dense

Fl to 2.5 cm

Fl to 2.2 cm

Fl 2 cm

Parasite on gorse, broom. Top ptl-tube lip unlobed, stamens join ptl tube, yellow stigmas. *Ht:* to 80 cm; *D:* W; *Fl:* 5–7

Parasite on greater knapweed. Stigmas yellow, stms attached 5 mm above ptl-tube base. *Ht:* 50 cm; *D:* T (not N); *Fl:* 6–7

Parasite on thistles. Fls v curved at base, have small black glands at edges and purple stigmas. *Ht:* 35 cm; *D:* T (not N); *Fl:* 6–8

Common broomrape	Purple broomrape	Toothwort

O. minor

O. purpurea

Lathraea squamaria

Stigmas
purple

Spike
loose

Infl
1-sided

Stems
bluish

Ptl tube
2-lipped

Parasite on clover,
catsear. Ptl tube
curved. *Ht:* 35 cm; *D:*
W, S, C; *Fl:* 6–9

Parasite on yarrow.
Each 3 cm fl has 3
bracts. *Ht:* 30 cm; *D:*
T (not N); *Fl:* 6–7

Parasite on hazel, elm.
Spl tube 4-lobed. *Ht:*
20 cm; *D:* T (not N);
Fl: 4–5

Butterwort family Lentibulariaceae

Insectivorous plants with sticky leaves or bladder traps. Flowers have
5-lobed or 2-lipped sepal tubes, spurred 2-lipped petal tubes, 2 stamens and 2 carpels.

Common butterwort | Large-flowered butterwort

Pinguicula vulgaris

P. grandiflora

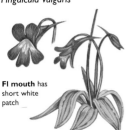

Fl mouth has
long white
patch

Fl mouth has
short white
patch

Oval lvs to 8 cm. Fl stks; 10 cm; fls
to 1.5 cm, lower lip v cleft, spur
6 mm. *D:* N, W, C; *Fl:* 5–7

Oval lvs to 20 cm. Fl stks 15 cm;
fls 2 cm, shallow cleft in lower lip,
1 cm spur. *D:* SW; *Fl:* 5–6

Pale butterwort | Alpine butterwort

P. lusitanica

Fl delicate

P. alpina

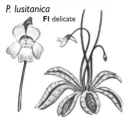

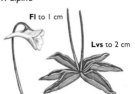

Fl to 1 cm

Lvs to 2 cm

Leaves to 2 cm. Fl stks 10 cm; fls
to 7 mm, spur 3 mm, cylindrical,
pointed tip. *D:* W; *Fl:* 6–10

One or 2 yellow spots at fl mouth,
spur conical, downcurved, to 3 mm.
Ht: 7 cm; *D:* C, Arct; *Fl:* 5–8

Hairy butterwort

Pinguicula villosa

Fl to 9 mm

Very like *P. alpina* (p. 129) but fl stks stickily hry. *Ht:* 7 cm; *D:* Fennoscand; *Fl:* 5–8

Lesser bladderwort

Utricularia minor

Fl stks to 15 cm

Fl to 8 mm

Slender stems to 25 cm have bladders, some stems green, some colourless in mud. Lvs lobed, palmate. *D:* T; *Fl:* 6–9

Greater bladderwort

U. vulgaris

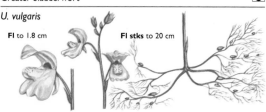

Fl to 1.8 cm

Fl stks to 20 cm

Free-floating aquatic. Stems to 45 cm, all green with bladders. Lvs pinnately cut into fine-toothed segs. *D:* T; *Fl:* 7–8

Plantain family Plantaginaceae

Herbs with leaves in basal rosettes. Tiny flowers in dense heads have petal and sepal tubes with 4 fused parts, and 4 stamens joining the petal tube. The fruit is a capsule.

Ribwort plantain

Plantago lanceolata

Lvs 3–5 parallel veins

Perennial; lvs long, narrow, to 15 cm. Infl head to 2 cm long, on deeply furrowed stk to 40 cm. *D:* T (not far N); *Fl:* 4–8

Greater plantain

P. major

Fl head to 15 cm

Fl stk to 15 cm, not furrowed

Leaves to 15 cm long and almost as broad, narrow abruptly to long stk. *Ht:* 20 cm; *D:* T; *Fl:* 5–9

Hoary plantain | Buckshorn plantain

P. media | *P. coronopus*

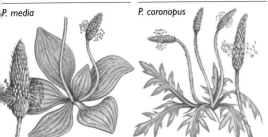

Softly hry lvs to 6 cm, v short-stkd. Infl head to 6 cm, on long stk to 30 cm. *D:* T; *Fl:* 5–8 | Leaves to 6 cm pinnately cut into narrow segs. Infl head to 4 cm on 5 cm stk. *Ht:* 10 cm; *D:* T; *Fl:* 5–7

Branched plantain | Sea plantain | Shoreweed

P. arenaria | *P. maritima* | *Littorella uniflora*

Infl long-stkd

Scrambles to 30 cm. Lvs narrow, lower lvs have axillary shs; infl 1 cm. *D:* T; *Fl:* 7–8 | Tuft of succ narrow lvs with 3–5 veins. Infl head 4 cm. *Ht:* 13 cm; *D:* T; *Fl:* 6–8 | Fine lvs; has stolons; ♂, ♀ fls sep in same or diff heads. *Ht:* 7 cm; *D:* W, C; *Fl:* 6–8

Moschatel family Adoxaceae

Uppermost flower has 2 joined sepals, 4 petals and 4 stamens. Side flowers have 3 sepals, 5 petals and 5 stamens.

Moschatel

Adoxa moschatellina
Fl stk unbranched

Infl 6 mm diam

Lvs 3-lobed, long-stalked

The only species in the family, a delicate herb to 10 cm with creeping rhizome. Infl of 5 fls has cubic form. *D:* T; *Fl:* 4–5

Honeysuckle family Caprifoliaceae

Woody or herbaceous plants with opposite leaves. Flowers have 5 petals and sepals and 5 stamens attached to the petal tube which may be 2-lipped.

Honeysuckle

Lonicera periclymenum

Fr globular

Perfoliate honeysuckle

L. caprifolium

As *L. periclymenum* but glaucous lf prs fused below, some fls in lf axils. *Ht:* 5 m; *D:* S, EC; *Fl:* 5–6

Twin flower

Linnaea borealis

Lvs 1 cm, short stkd

Woody climber to 6 m. Fls to 5 cm in terminal infl are 2-lipped, top lip 4-lobed, lower unlobed. *D:* W, C, S; *Fl:* 6–9

Mat-forming evergreen. Fls 8 mm, nodding, fl stks delicate to 7 cm. *D:* S mts, N; *Fl:* 6–8

Valerian family Valerianaceae

Opposite-leaved herbs. Small 5-lobed funnel-shaped flowers have sepals indistinct from feathery attachment to fruit.

Common valerian

Valeriana officinalis   **Infl** dense

Lvs to 20 cm

Red valerian

Centranthus ruber

Fls to 1 cm

Lvs 10 cm, glaucous

Erect per to 1.5 m. Lvs pinnate, lobed, basal lvs stkd. Fls 5 mm, 3 stamens. *D:* T; *Fl:* 6–8

Leaves oval. Fls white or red, narrow, spurred, 1 protruding stamen. *Ht:* 60 cm; *D:* S; *Fl:* 6–8

Valeriana dioica *Valerianella locusta*

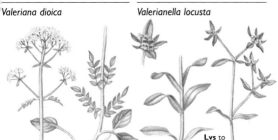

Lvs to
7 cm

Has stolons. Lf blades to 3 cm, basal unlobed, stkd, upper unstkd, pinnate. ♂, ♀ parts in sep fls. *Ht:* 20 cm; *D:* W, C; *Fl:* 5–6

Erect, branched ann to 40 cm. Lvs unlobed. Fls in small, dense heads surrounded by narrow bracts, spls indistinct. *D:* T; *Fl:* 4–6

Scabious family Dipsacaceae

Opposite-leaved herbs with dense, round flower heads. Sepals are inconspicuous but each 4–5-lobed flower is surrounded by bracts. There are 2 or 4 stamens.

Field scabious	Wood scabious	Devilsbit scabious
Knautia arvensis	*K. dipsacifolia*	*Succisa pratensis*

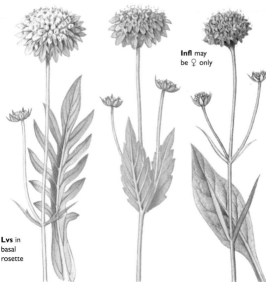

Infl may
be ♀ only

Lvs in
basal
rosette

Robust per to 1 m; lvs lobed, hry; infl 4 cm diam, outer fls larger than inner, bristly spls. *D:* T; *Fl:* 7–9

Like *K. arvensis* but taller. Stem lvs not lobed, serrate. Infl 3 cm diam. *Ht:* 1.2 m; *D:* C mts; *Fl:* 6–9

Unlobed lvs, midribs white. Infl 2 cm diam, all fls same size. Ptl tube to 7 mm. *Ht:* 80 cm; *D:* T; *Fl:* 6–10

Small scabious Teasel Small teasel

Scabiosa columbaria | *Dipsacus fullonum* | *D. pilosus*

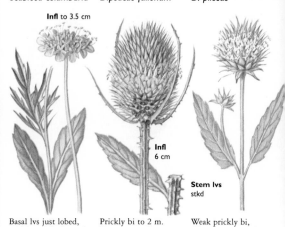

Infl to 3.5 cm

Infl 6 cm

Stem lvs stkd

Basal lvs just lobed, mid lvs v lobed, top lvs finely cut; outer fls largest. *Ht:* 55 cm; *D:* T (not N); *Fl:* 7–8

Prickly bi to 2 m. Narrow stem lvs encircle stem; infl has long, spiny bracts. *D:* S, W, C; Fl: 7–8

Weak prickly bi, ridged stems to 1.2 m. Infl *c.* 2 cm, round, drooping in bud. *D:* W, C, *Fl:* 8

Bellflower family Campanulaceae

Herbs with a milky sap and simple, alternate leaves. Bell-shaped, symmetrical flowers have 5 stamens. The family includes the lobelias with asymmetrical two-lipped flowers.

Harebell | Spreading bellflower | Clustered bellflower

Campanula rotundifolia | *C. patula* | *C. glomerata*

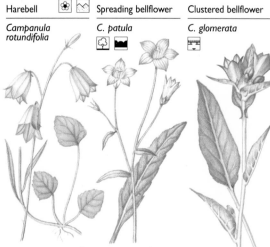

Delicate hrlss per to 40 cm. Round, stkd lvs borne on prostrate shs, narrow unstkd lvs on fl shs. Fls nodding, 1.5 cm. *D:* T; *Fl:* 7–9

Rough per to 60 cm. Lower lvs short-stkd. Infl much-branched; bracts in middle of fl stks, fls erect, 2 cm. *D:* T; *Fl:* 7–9

Short, hry per to 20 cm. Basal lvs long-stkd. Fls uprt, unstkd in dense clusters. *D:* T (not N); *Fl:* 5–9

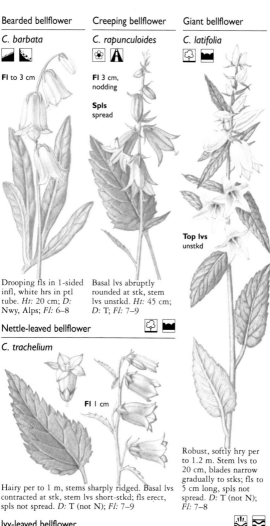

Bearded bellflower

C. barbata

Fl to 3 cm

Drooping fls in 1-sided infl, white hrs in ptl tube. *Ht:* 20 cm; *D:* Nwy, Alps; *Fl:* 6–8

Creeping bellflower

C. rapunculoides

Fl 3 cm, nodding

Spls spread

Basal lvs abruptly rounded at stk, stem lvs unstkd. *Ht:* 45 cm; *D:* T; *Fl:* 7–9

Giant bellflower

C. latifolia

Top lvs unstkd

Robust, softly hry per to 1.2 m. Stem lvs to 20 cm, blades narrow gradually to stks; fls to 5 cm long, spls not spread. *D:* T (not N); *Fl:* 7–8

Nettle-leaved bellflower

C. trachelium

Fl 1 cm

Hairy per to 1 m, stems sharply ridged. Basal lvs contracted at stk, stem lvs short-stkd; fls erect, spls not spread. *D:* T (not N); *Fl:* 7–9

Ivy-leaved bellflower

Wahlenbergia hederacea

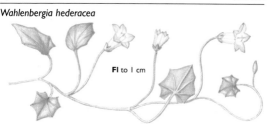

Fl to 1 cm

Delicate creeping per, sprawling stems to 30 cm. Lvs ivy-shaped, long stkd. Slim fl stks to 4 cm, fls nodding. *D:* W; *Fl:* 7–8

Sheepsbit scabious

Jasione montana

  Infl 2 cm diam

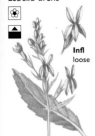

Lvs 5 cm

Plant softly hry

Small fls in dense head surrounded by short bracts. *Ht:* 35 cm; *D:* T; *Fl:* 5–8

Round-headed rampion

Phyteuma orbiculare

Infl 1.5 cm diam

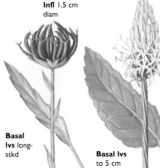

Basal lvs long-stkd

Spherical infl, ptl lobes tubular below, then spread. *Ht:* 35 cm; *D:* T (not N); *Fl:* 7–8

Spiked rampion

P. spicatum

  Fls c. 1 cm

Basal lvs to 5 cm

Flowers in 6 cm spike, ptl lobes spread as fl ages. *Ht:* 60 cm; *D:* T (not N); *Fl:* 7–8

Heath lobelia

Lobelia urens

Infl loose

Many serrate lvs to 7 cm. Ptl tube to 1.5 cm, 2-lipped. *Ht:* 45 cm; *D:* W; *Fl:* 8–9

Water lobelia

L. dortmanna

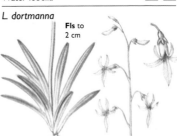

Fls to 2 cm

Spreads by stolons. Tuft of narrow lvs to 4 cm. Fl stems to 60 cm emerge from water. Infl loose, fls 2-lipped, nodding. *D:* N, NC; *Fl:* 7–8

Venus's looking glass

Legousia hybrida

Spls erect in fr

Lvs unstkd to 3 cm

Has stiff hrs. Lf edges wavy. Fls uprt, ovary elongate, spls 2 × ptls. *Ht:* 20 cm; *D:* W, S; *Fl:* 5–8

Large Venus's looking glass

L. speculum-veneris

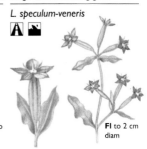

Fl to 2 cm diam

Much-branched ann to 40 cm. Ptls as long as spls and ovary, spls spread in fr. *D:* SW, SC; *Fl:* 5–7

Daisy family Asteraceae

Usually herbs, but a huge and variable family. Leaves have no stipules.
Small flowers (florets) are in dense heads on the flat top of the inflores-
cence stalk and surrounded by one or more rows of sepal-like bracts.
Florets may be all alike (as thistles) or the outer ones may be longer (as
daisies) and either tubular (disc florets) or strap-shaped (ray florets).
Each ovary has one cell.

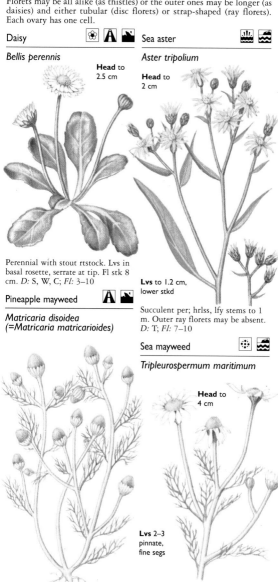

Daisy

Bellis perennis

Head to
2.5 cm

Perennial with stout rtstock. Lvs in
basal rosette, serrate at tip. Fl stk 8
cm. *D*: S, W, C; *Fl*: 3–10

Pineapple mayweed

Matricaria disoidea
(=Matricaria matricarioides)

Aromatic herb to 30 cm. Lvs 2–3
pinnate, fine segs. Heads have disc
florets only. *D*: T; *Fl*: 6–7

Sea aster

Aster tripolium

Head to
2 cm

Lvs to 1.2 cm,
lower stkd

Succulent per; hrlss, lfy stems to 1
m. Outer ray florets may be absent.
D: T, *Fl*: 7–10

Sea mayweed

Tripleurospermum maritimum

Head to
4 cm

Lvs 2–3
pinnate,
fine segs

Biennial or per, stout rtstock.
Common weed *M. perforata* sim but
ann. *Ht*: 50 cm; *D*: W, N; *Fl*: 7–9

137

Golden rod

Solidago virgaurea

Stem lvs toothed

Erect, few brs. Fl heads to 1 cm in terminal clusters. *Ht:* 55 cm; *D:* T; *Fl:* 7–9

Blue fleabane

Erigeron acer

Dense, long hrs on stem and lvs. Many ray florets in 2 or more rows. *Ht:* 30 cm; *D:* T; *Fl:* 7–8

Basal lvs to 7 cm

Canadian fleabane

Conyza canadensis

Stems branched to 1 m, many narrow lvs to 4 cm. Heads 4 mm, sev rows ray florets. *D:* T; *Fl:* 8–9

Gallant soldier

Galinsoga parviflora

Many brs; serrate lvs in opp prs. Oval bracts round 5-rayed heads. Ht: 60 cm; *D:* T (not N); *Fl:* 5–11

Ploughman's spikenard

Inula conyza

Robust bi or per, red stems to 1.3 m; heads in loose terminal gps, no rays, narrow bracts. *D:* W, S, C; *Fl:* 7–9

Fleabane

I. britannica

Erect per to 60 cm, usually v hry. Heads to 4 cm, usually sol, bracts narrow, hry. *D:* S, C; *Fl:* 7–8

138

Golden samphire

I. crithmoides

Lvs to
6 cm

Hairless, succ per; lvs
fleshy, 3-toothed at tip.
Heads have many ray
florets. *Ht:* 70 cm; *D:*
S, W; *Fl:* 7–8

Leopardsbane

Doronicum pardalianches

Basal lvs hry, heart-
shaped. Heads to 6 cm,
single row large ray
florets. *Ht:* 60 cm; *D:*
W; *Fl:* 5–7

Elecampane

I. helenium

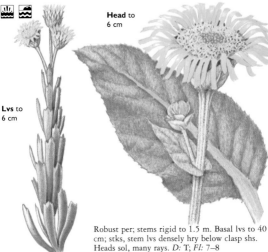

Head to
6 cm

Robust per; stems rigid to 1.5 m. Basal lvs to 40
cm; stks, stem lvs densely hry below clasp shs.
Heads sol, many rays. *D:* T; *Fl:* 7–8

Common fleabane

Pulicaria dysenterica

Head to
3 cm

Plant
perennial

Stem lvs wavy-edged,
v hry below; 1 row ray
florets 2 × disc florets.
Ht: 40 cm; *D:* S, W, C;
Fl: 8–9

Small fleabane

P. vulgaris

Head 1 cm

Plant
ann, hry

Stem lvs not rounded
at base. Ray florets 1
row, no longer than
disc ones. *Ht:* 30 cm;
D: T (not N); *Fl:* 8–9

Corn chamomile

Anthemis arvensis

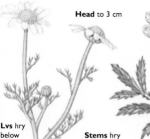

Head to 3 cm

Lvs hry below

Stems hry

Leaves v cut, top seg linear. Scales between disc florets. *Ht:* 40 cm; *D:* T (not far N); *Fl:* 6–7

Ox-eye daisy

Leucanthemum vulgare

Basal lvs serrate

Erect stems to 70 cm plus non-flowering lfy rosettes. Heads sol, long rays to 5 cm. *D:* T; *Fl:* 6–8

Coltsfoot

Tussilago farfara

Lvs to 20 cm

Round, toothed lvs appear after fls. All florets have strap-shaped ligule. *Ht:* 10 cm; *D:* T; *Fl:* 3–4

Tansy

Tanacetum vulgare

Lvs to 25 cm

Strong-smelling per. Lvs pinnate, lobes toothed, no ray florets. *Ht:* 80 cm; *D:* T; *Fl:* 7–9

Corn marigold

Chrysanthemum segetum

Lvs to 8 cm

Erect, hrlss ann to 50 cm; lvs succ, coarsely toothed. Heads to 6.5 cm, sol, long-stkd. *D:* W; *Fl:* 6–8

Purple coltsfoot

Homogyne alpina

Basal lvs kidney-shaped, toothed, purple below. Heads sol, to 1.5 cm. *Ht:* 20 cm; *D:* W, C, S; *Fl:* 5–8

Dandelion

Taraxacum officinale

Leaf lobes curl back; infl stk unbranched, 2 rows bracts, outer ones bent back. *Ht:* 40 cm; *D:* T; *Fl:* 3–10

Spotted catsear

H. maculata

Leaves to 15 cm, hry, spotted purple. No scale bracts on infl stk. *Ht:* 60 cm; *D:* T (not N, NW); *Fl:* 6–8

Slender thistle

Cardus tenuiflorus

Uprt stems with spiny wings reaching to infl heads. Lvs cottony white beneath. Infl heads cylindrical rather than globular. *Ht:* 15 cm–1.2 m; *D:* W; *Fl:* 6–8

Autumn hawkbit

Leontodon autumnalis

Perennial with branched fl stems arising from basal rosette of hairless, deeply-lobed lvs. Fls reddish beneath. *Ht:* 5–60 cm; *D:* T; *Fl:* 6–10

Catsear

H. radicata

Unbranched, hrs on lvs. Top of branched fl stk swollen, has scale bracts. *Ht:* 50 cm; *D:* T (not NE); *Fl:* 6–9

Smooth catsear

Hypochoeris glabra

Lvs nearly hrlss

Annual to 40 cm. The heads open only in full sun, florets just as long as bracts. *D:* T (not N); *Fl:* 6–10

Rough hawkbit

Leontodon hispidus

Head to 4 cm

Dense, forked hrs all over. Infl stk hry, no scales among florets unlike *L. autumnalis.* *Ht:* 45 cm; *D:* T; *Fl:* 6–9

Ragwort

Senecio jacobaea

Alpine ragwort

S. oratus

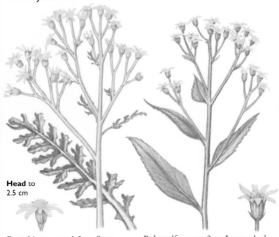

Head to 2.5 cm

Erect bi or per to 1.5 m. Stem ridged, often with long hrs; basal lvs deeply lobed in rosette, stem lvs pinnate. *D:* T; *Fl:* 6–10

Robust lfy per to 2 m. Lvs toothed, hry below. Heads 3 cm, densely gpd, bracts in 1 row as most *Senecio* spp. *D:* C, S; *Fl:* 7–9

Groundsel

S. vulgaris

Oxford ragwort

S. squalidus

Broad-leaved ragwort

S. fluviatilis

Stks of lower lvs winged

Erect ann to 45 cm. Lvs lobed, clasping, may have woolly hrs. Heads to 1 cm, rarely with ray florets. *D:* T; *Fl:* 1–12. *S. sylvaticus* sim but always with rays.

Hairless, erect ann to 30 cm. Heads to 2 cm in irregular gps have ray florets. *Ht:* 25 cm; *D:* C, S; *Fl:* 5–12

Has stolons; uprt shs to 1.5 m. Lvs hrlss, serrate to 20 cm. Heads 3 cm, have rays. *D:* C, E; *Fl:* 7–9

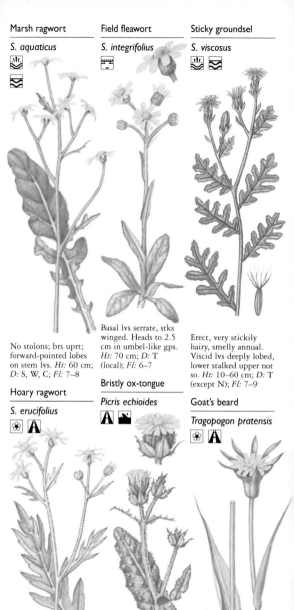

Marsh ragwort

S. aquaticus

No stolons; brs uprt; forward-pointed lobes on stem lvs. *Ht:* 60 cm; *D:* S, W, C; *Fl:* 7–8

Field fleawort

S. integrifolius

Basal lvs serrate, stks winged. Heads to 2.5 cm in umbel-like gps. *Ht:* 70 cm; *D:* T (local); *Fl:* 6–7

Sticky groundsel

S. viscosus

Erect, very stickily hairy, smelly annual. Viscid lvs deeply lobed, lower stalked upper not so. *Ht:* 10–60 cm; *D:* T (except N); *Fl:* 7–9

Hoary ragwort

S. erucifolius

Has stolons. Stem lvs hry below, top lobe pointed. *Ht:* 1 m; *D:* T (Not NW); *Fl:* 7–8

Bristly ox-tongue

Picris echioides

Plant bristly

Head has 3–5 lfy outer bracts, all florets have ligules. *Ht:* 90 cm; *D:* S; *Fl:* 6–10

Goat's beard

Tragopogon pratensis

Linear, pointed lvs; whorl bracts longer than florets. *Ht:* to 70 cm; *D:* T; *Fl:* 6–7

Smooth hawksbeard

Crepis capillaris

Stem lvs arrow-shaped below; infl 1 cm, bracts not spread. *Ht:* 70 cm; *D:* W, C, S; *Fl:* 6–9

Beaked hawksbeard

C. vesicaria **Head to 2.5 cm**

Bracts spreading. Fr beaked, pappus longer than bracts. *Ht:* 60 cm; *D:* S, C, W; *Fl:* 5–7

Marsh hawksbeard

C. paludosa

Erect to 90 cm. Heads to 2.5 cm, bracts hry, pappus brown bristles. *D:* N, C; *Fl:* 7–9

Orange hawkweed

Pilosella aurantiaca

Heads brown or orange-red

Has stolons; simple hrs on lvs. Fl stks to 65 cm have dark hrs. *D:* N, C Mts; *Fl:* 6–8

Mouse-ear hawkweed

P. officinarum

Leaf hrs sparse above, dense below. Red stripe on ligule back. *Ht:* 20 cm; *D:* T; *Fl:* 5–8

Alpine hawkweed

P. alpina

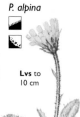

Lvs to 10 cm

Stems hry to 15 cm; lf hrs long, simple. Large heads to 3 cm. *D:* N, C; *Fl:* 7–8

Leafy hawkweed

Hieracium umbellatum

Stems uprt, lfy to 1 m. Crowded stem lvs to 15 cm below, smaller above. *D:* T; *Fl:* 8–9

Perennial sow thistle

Sonchus arvensis

Head to 5 cm

Stem sticky, hry

Marsh sow thistle

S. palustris

Head c. 4 cm

Bract hrs black, sticky

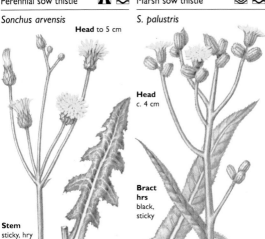

Robust per to 1.5 m. Round lobes on stem lvs encircle stem. Bract hrs yellow, sticky. *D:* T; *Fl:* 7–10

Ridged stems to 3 m. Lf lobes long, lance-shaped, spread, bases pointed. *D:* T (not N); *Fl:* 7–9

Smooth sow thistle

S. oleraceus

Stems ridged

Prickly sow thistle

S. asper

Scorzonera

Scorzonera laciniata

Hairless ann to 1.5 m. Lvs spiny, pointed lobes encircle stem. Heads to 2.5 cm, fr rough. *D:* T; *Fl:* 6–8

Like *S. oleraceus* but prickly lvs have round lobes encircling stem. Fr smooth. *Ht:* 1 m; *D:* T; *Fl:* 6–8

Scrambles to 60 cm; lvs pinnate, lobes narrow or round. Sev rows of bracts; fr base tubular. *D:* C, S; *Fl:* 4–7

145

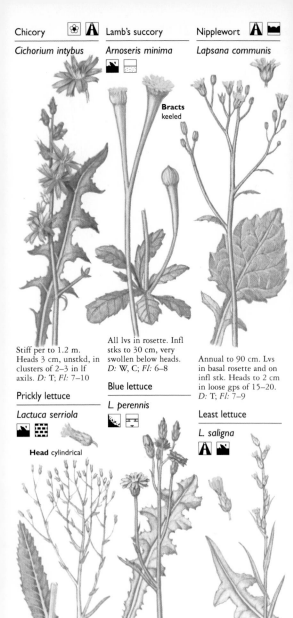

Chicory

Cichorium intybus

Stiff per to 1.2 m. Heads 3 cm, unstkd, in clusters of 2–3 in lf axils. *D:* T; *Fl:* 7–10

Prickly lettuce

Lactuca serriola

Head cylindrical

Stiff stems to 1.5 m; stem lvs uprt, spiny at edges and on white midrib. *D:* T; *Fl:* 7–9

Lamb's succory

Arnoseris minima

Bracts keeled

All lvs in rosette. Infl stks to 30 cm, very swollen below heads. *D:* W, C; *Fl:* 6–8

Blue lettuce

L. perennis

Erect per to 80 cm. Spineless lvs have narrow lobes. Heads to 4 cm diam, cylindrical on long stks to 8 cm. *D:* T; *Fl:* 5–8

Nipplewort

Lapsana communis

Annual to 90 cm. Lvs in basal rosette and on infl stk. Heads to 2 cm in loose gps of 15–20. *D:* T; *Fl:* 7–9

Least lettuce

L. saligna

Basal lvs lobed

Stem lvs linear, not spiny, lobed at base. Heads in spike. *Ht:* 1 m; *D:* S, C; *Fl:* 7–8

Wall lettuce

Mycelis muralis

Stks of lower lvs winged

Erect per to 1 m. Lower lvs have big top lobe itself 3-lobed; head of 5 ligulate fls. *D:* T; *Fl:* 7–9

Globe thistle

Echinops sphaerocephalus

Plant spiny

Leaves pinnately lobed, hry esp below. Spherical head to 6 cm diam. *D:* S, C; *Fl:* 6–9

Lesser burdock

Arctium minus

Plant bushy

Bushy bi to 1.3 m. Lvs unlobed, lower lf stks hollow. Many hooked bracts in heads. *D:* T; *Fl:* 7–9

Purple lettuce

Prenanthes purpurea

Leaves elliptical, glaucous to 80 cm. Heads 2–5 narrow cylindric fls. *Ht:* 1 m; *D:* C, S mts; *Fl:* 7–9

Milk thistle

Silybum marianum

Head to 5 cm

Bracts have big, spread spines

Lvs lobed

Stems ridged, woolly, unwinged to 1.2 m. White patches on veins of spiny lvs. *D:* S, W; *Fl:* 6–8

Greater burdock

A. lappa

As *A. minus* but basal lvs broader, lf stks solid. Fls fewer, long-stkd heads 3 cm. *Ht:* 1.2 m; *D:* T (not far N); *Fl:* 7–9. *A. tomentosum* sim, with cobweb-like hrs in fl head.

Carlina acaulis

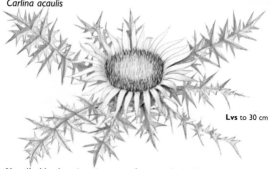

Lvs to 30 cm

Unstalked heads to 5 cm in centre of rosette of spiny lvs. Inner bracts silvery white, spread. Fls white to brown. *Ht:* 30 cm; *D:* S; *Fl:* 5–9

Carline thistle

Spear thistle

Carlina vulgaris

Cirsium vulgare

Inner bracts
ray-like

Basal lvs
prickly, hry
to 30 cm

Stems to 1.5 m, spiny wings discontinuous in broken patches. Globular heads to 5 cm. *D:* T; *Fl:* 7–10

Erect bi to 60 cm. Rosette of woolly lvs in 1st year lost before 4 cm fls arise in 2nd. *D:* T; *Fl:* 7–10

Cabbage thistle

Stemless thistle

C. acaule   **Head** to 4 cm

C. oleraceum

Head to 4 cm

Lvs elliptical,
deeply cut

Rosette of spiny lvs to 15 cm. Sev central fl heads on v short stks. *Ht:* 20 cm; *D:* C, W, S; *Fl:* 7–9

Stems uprt, grooved, unwinged to 1.2 m. Stem lvs unlobed, top lvs extend over heads. *D:* T; *Fl:* 7–9

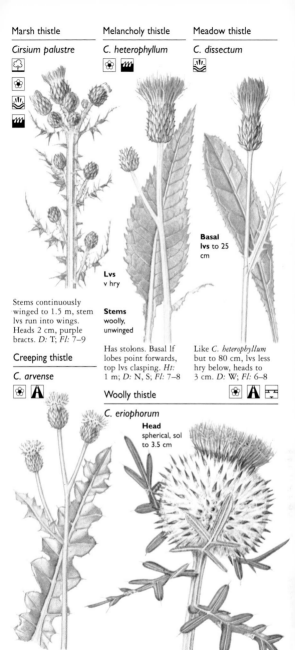

Marsh thistle

Cirsium palustre

Stems continuously winged to 1.5 m, stem lvs run into wings. Heads 2 cm, purple bracts. *D*: T; *Fl*: 7–9

Creeping thistle

C. arvense

Patch-forming per to 1 m. Stems lfy, not winged. Heads may be sol. *D*: T; *Fl*: 7–9

Melancholy thistle

C. heterophyllum

Lvs v hry

Stems woolly, unwinged

Has stolons. Basal lf lobes point forwards, top lvs clasping. *Ht*: 1 m; *D*: N, S; *Fl*: 7–8

Woolly thistle

C. eriophorum

Head spherical, sol to 3.5 cm

Robust bi. Stems ridged, unwinged to 1.5 m. Basal lvs 60 cm, pinnate lobed, cottony below. Dense woolly hrs on bracts. *D*: W, C; *Fl*: 7–9

Meadow thistle

C. dissectum

Basal lvs to 25 cm

Like *C. heterophyllum* but to 80 cm, lvs less hry below, heads to 3 cm. *D*: W; *Fl*: 6–8

Welted thistle

Carduus acanthoides

Plant covered with cottony white hrs

Winged stems to 1.5 m, wings stop well below unstkd fl heads to 2.5 cm. *D:* T; *Fl:* 6–8

Alpine saw wort

Saussurea alpina

Lvs woolly below

Rosettes of non-spiny, serrate lvs to 18 cm. Stems cottony, heads 2 cm in small gps. *Ht:* 30 cm; *D:* N, S; *Fl:* 8–9

Musk thistle

C. nutans

Heads nodding to 5 cm

Stems woolly, winged except below heads. Bracts spiny, spread. *Ht:* 80 cm; *D:* W, C; *Fl:* 5–8

Winged thistle

C. crispus

Infl stks to 8 cm

As *C. acanthoides* but stems near hrlss, wings narrow. *Ht:* 1 m; *D:* T (not UK); *Fl:* 6–10

Cotton thistle

Onopordum acanthium

Head to 5 cm

Stems winged, woolly to 1.5 m. Globular heads, woolly bracts. *D:* C, S; *Fl:* 7–9

Alpine sow thistle

Cicerbita alpina

Ridged stem to 2 m, reddish hrs above. Heads 2 cm, stickily hry in loose gps. *D:* N, S; *Fl:* 7–9

Greater knapweed

Centaurea scabiosa

Head to 5 cm

Stems grooved

Basal lvs pinnate. Outer florets big, spread. *Ht:* 70 cm; *D:* T; *Fl:* 7–9. *C. jacea* sim, brown bracts.

Perennial cornflower

C. montana

Head to 1.5 cm

Lvs unlobed

Creeping, rhizomatous; winged stems to 80 cm. Outer florets blue, inner purple. *D:* C mts; *Fl:* 5–7

Cornflower

C. cyanus

Basal lvs to 20 cm

Stiff, cottony stems to 90 cm. Basal lvs pinnate lobed, hry; heads to 3 cm. *D:* T; *Fl:* 6–8

Black knapweed

C. nigra

Tough, branching per, stems uprt, grooved, hry to 90 cm. Basal lvs unlobed. Heads to 4 cm diam, no spreading florets. Bracts dark at tips. *D:* W, C, S; *Fl:* 6–9

Rough star thistle

C. aspera

Erect to 90 cm. Heads sol, 2.5 cm; bracts have finger-like spines spread at tips. D: SW; *Fl:* 7–9

Red star thistle

C. calcitrapa

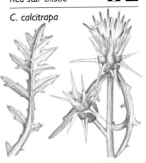

Pinnate lvs, lobes spined. Bracts spreading to 2.5 cm with 1 spine. *Ht:* 45 cm; *D:* S, W, C; *Fl:* 7–9

Serratula tinctoria   *Eupatorium cannabinum*

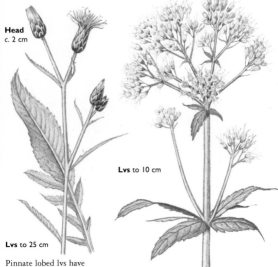

Head
c. 2 cm

Lvs to 10 cm

Lvs to 25 cm

Pinnate lobed lvs have finely pointed teeth. ♂, ♀ fls separate. *Ht:* 65 cm; *D:* T (not NE); *Fl:* 7–9

Robust, uprt per to 1.2 m. Lvs opp, 3-lobed, lobes toothed. Heads in dense terminal gps each with *c.* 6 tubular florets. *D:* T; *Fl:* 7–9

Mountain everlasting   Common cudweed

Antennaria dioica   *Filago vulgaris*

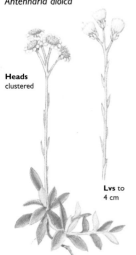

Heads
clustered

Lvs to
4 cm

Lvs to 2 cm

Has stolons. Lvs in rosettes have dense white hrs below. Bracts dense, woolly. *Ht:* 15 cm; *D:* T; *Fl:* 6–7

Woolly uprt ann to 35 cm. Lvs uprt, wavy, white hrs; 20–40 heads form dense group. *D:* S, W, C; *Fl:* 7–8

Small cudweed	Heath cudweed	Helichrysum

F. minima

Gnaphalium sylvaticum

H. arenarium

Head
2 mm

Basal lvs
to 7 cm,
obovate

Delicate ann to 15 cm; lvs to 1 cm. Heads 3 mm, 3–6 in a cluster. *D:* T (not NE); *Fl:* 6–9

Basal lvs to 8 cm. Axillary heads in loose spikes. *Ht:* 45 cm; *D:* T; *Fl:* 7–9

Dwarf cudweed

G. supina

Heads form
short spike

Prostrate per, forms small tussocks. Lvs woolly. Fl shs to 12 cm. *D:* N, S, C; *Fl:* 7

Hairy per; stem lvs short, linear. Heads globular, bracts orange-yellow. *Ht:* 20 cm; *D:* S, C; *Fl:* 7–9

Marsh cudweed

G. uliginosum

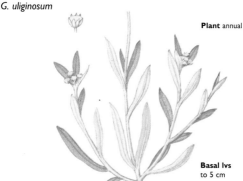

Plant annual

Basal lvs
to 5 cm

Many brs from base, 3–10 heads in dense group, v long lvs at infl base. *Ht:* 10 cm; *D:* T; *Fl:* 7–8

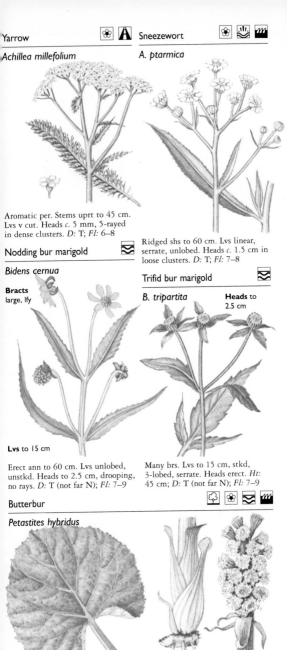

Yarrow 🏵 🅰

Achillea millefolium

Aromatic per. Stems uprt to 45 cm. Lvs v cut. Heads *c.* 5 mm, 5-rayed in dense clusters. *D:* T; *Fl:* 6–8

Sneezewort 🏵 〰 🌿

A. ptarmica

Ridged shs to 60 cm. Lvs linear, serrate, unlobed. Heads *c.* 1.5 cm in loose clusters. *D:* T; *Fl:* 7–8

Nodding bur marigold 〰

Bidens cernua

Bracts large, lfy

Erect ann to 60 cm. Lvs unlobed, unstkd. Heads to 2.5 cm, drooping, no rays. *D:* T (not far N); *Fl:* 7–9

Lvs to 15 cm

Trifid bur marigold 〰

B. tripartita

Heads to 2.5 cm

Many brs. Lvs to 15 cm, stkd, 3-lobed, serrate. Heads erect. *Ht:* 45 cm; *D:* T (not far N); *Fl:* 7–9

Butterbur 🌳 🏵 〰 🌿

Petasites hybridus

Rhizomatous per. Lvs to 90 cm. Fl shs to 40 cm. Serrate lvs appear after fl shs. Heads in dense gps, ♂, ♀ separate. *D:* T (not N); *Fl:* 3–5

Mugwort   Field wormwood

Artemisia vulgaris

A. campestris

Head to 4 mm

Head to 4 mm

Stem has scattered hrs

Tufted aromatic per to 1.2 m. Lvs pinnate-lobed, pointed, dark and hrlss above, white, woolly below. Heads oval. *D:* T; *Fl:* 7–9

Unscented; creeping per to 60 cm. Lvs v cut into narrow linear segs, hry at first then hrlss. Heads globular. *D:* T (not NW); *Fl:* 8–9

Wormwood   Sea wormwood   Cotton weed

A. absinthium

Seriphidium maritimum

Otanthus maritimus

Head to 2 mm

Aromatic per to 90 cm. Like *A. vulgaris* but lf segs more rounded, silky hrs on both sides. Heads globular or bell-shaped. *D:* T; *Fl:* 7–8

Very aromatic per to 50 cm. White woolly hrs all over lvs and stems, heads drooping. *D:* W, N; *Fl:* 8–9

Woody-based per to 30 cm, stems densely woolly, white. Lvs not lobed, felty. Heads to 9 mm have felty white bracts. *D:* W; *Fl:* 8–9

155

Water plantain family Alismataceae

Aquatic or wetland herbs with unlobed, stalked, sometimes floating leaves. Flowers have 3 sepals and petals and 6 or 3 stamens. There are usually many free carpels.

Common water plantain

Alisma plantago-aquatica

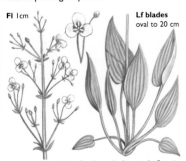

Fl 1cm

Lf blades oval to 20 cm

Leaves long-stkd. Infl v branched, carpels flat, 1 whorl. *Ht:* 80 cm; *D:* T (not far N); *Fl:* 6–8

Floating water plantain

Luronium natans   **Lvs** 8 cm

Slim floating shs to 50 cm. Lvs long-stkd, fls sol, long-stkd in lf axils. *D:* W, C; *Fl:* 7–8

Star-fruit

Damasonium alisma

Fl 6 mm

Stems to 30 cm; 6–10 carpels in 1 whorl make spread star when ripe. *D:* SW; *Fl:* 6–8

Arrowhead

Sagittaria sagittifolia

Lf blade 15 cm

Fl 2 cm

Floating lvs oval, uprt arrow-shaped. ♂, ♀ separate, ♂ fls many stamens. *Ht:* 70 cm; *D:* T (not far N); *Fl:* 7–8

Lesser water plantain

Baldellia ranunculoides

Erect herb to 20 cm. Lf blades 3 cm. Fls 1.5 cm diam in umbel or 2 whorls, fl stks vary in length up to 10 cm; fr curved. *D:* W; *Fl:* 5–8

Flowering rush family Butomaceae
Frogbit family Hydrocharitaceae

Aquatic or wetland herbs. Flowering rushes have 3-petalled and sepalled flowers in umbels and 6–9 unjoined stamens and carpels. Frogbit flowers have 3 petals, 3 or no sepals, one to many stamens and 2–5 fused carpels.

Flowering rush

Water soldier

Butomus umbellatus

Stratiotes aloides

Dense lfy clusters, new plants develop on stolons. Lvs stiff, spiny-toothed. Fls to 4 cm on short shs. *Ht:* 40 cm; *D:* C, E; *Fl:* 6–8

Canadian pondweed

Elodea canadensis

Lvs to
1 cm

Hairless per. Lvs long, narrow, twisted. Fls *c.* 3 cm diam in an umbel with pointed bracts. *Ht:* 1 m; *D:* T (not NW); *Fl:* 7–9

Submerged stems to 3 m. Lvs 3 per whorl have tiny teeth. Fls 5 mm. *D:* T (not N); *Fl:* 5–10

Frogbit

Hydrocharis morsus-ranae

Fl 2 cm, above water

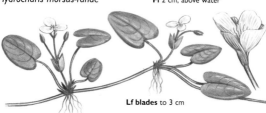

Lf blades to 3 cm

Floating herb to 3 m; rts in bunches with lvs. Floating lvs heart-shaped. Opp pair of bracts at fl stk-base. *D:* T (not N); *Fl:* 7–8

Eel grass family Zosteraceae

Marine grass-like herbs with creeping rhizomes. Flowers in dense spike are alternately male and female.

Eel grass

Zostera marina

Rhizomatous per to 60 cm. Lvs to 50 cm long by 1 cm broad, rounded at tips, sheathed at base. *Z. noltii* sim but lvs to 12 cm. *D:* T; *Fl:* 6–9

Pondweed family Potamogetonaceae

Flexible-stemmed aquatics. Floating leaves are broad, submerged ones narrow. Flowers have 4 bracts and 4 stamens.

Broad-leaved pondweed

Potamogeton natans

Spike to 8 cm

Stems to 5 m. Floating lf blades to 1.3 cm, joint at stk attachment. Lf stks winged. *D:* T; *Fl:* 5–9

Shining pondweed

P. lucens

Stems to 6 m. Submerged lvs to 20 cm, wavy edges, no floating lvs. *D:* T (not N); *Fl:* 6–9

Bog pondweed

P. polygonifolius

Spike to 4 cm

Stems to 60 cm. Floating lvs to 6 cm with large blunt stipules to 4 cm at base. *D:* W; *Fl:* 5–10

Opposite-leaved pondweed

Groenlandia densa

Lvs to 2.5 cm

Much branched stems to 30 cm; lvs in opp prs, toothed edges, all submerged. *D:* W; *Fl:* 5–9

Tasselweed family Ruppiaceae
Naiad family Najadaceae

Submerged aquatic herbs. Tasselweeds have hair-like leaves and flowers in umbels without sepals or petals. Naiads have whorled leaves and separate male and female flowers, the male with one stamen and a bract, female with 2–4 stigmas.

Beaked tasselweed	Slender naiad	Holly-leaved naiad
Ruppia maritima	*Najas flexilis*	*N. marina*

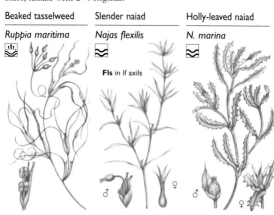

Fls in lf axils

Delicate per to 30 cm. Stems branched, lvs linear, fr strongly beaked. *D:* T; *Fl:* 7–9

Delicate ann to 30 cm. Lvs narrow, 2–3 per whorl, not toothed. *D:* T (local); *Fl:* 8–9

Submerged, stiff stems to 25 cm. Lvs spiny-toothed, mostly in opp prs. *D:* C; *Fl:* 7–8

Lily family Liliaceae

A diverse family of herbs. Flowers have 2 whorls of 3 petal-like parts, which may be fused or free, and 6 stamens. The ovary of 3 fused carpels is below the other flower parts.

Orange lily	Martagon lily
Lilium bulbiferum	*L. martagon*

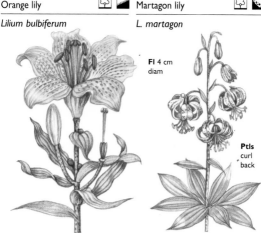

Fl 4 cm diam

Ptls curl back

Leaves linear, often bulbils in axils; 1–5 fls per gp, curled ptls. *Ht:* 50 cm; *D:* T; *Fl:* 6–7

Erect stems to 1 m. Lvs linear in widely separated whorls. Fls nodding. *D:* S, C, E; *Fl:* 8–9

159

Kerry lily

Simethis planifolia

All lvs basal, linear, to 45 cm. Infl loose with short bracts, infl stk to 45 cm; fl 2 cm. *Ht:* 1 m; *D:* W; *Fl:* 5–7

Snowdon lily

Lloydia serotina

Bulbous per; stems to 15 cm with 2–4 linear lvs. Fls 2 cm, 1–2 per sh, ptls veined. *D:* C, S, Wales; *Fl:* 6

May lily

Maianthemum bifolium

Stems have stiff white hrs above

Rhizomatous per to 20 cm. Lvs to 6 cm, heart-shaped. Infl dense, terminal; 8–15 fls with 4 ptls, 4 stamens, fr red. *D:* T; *Fl:* 5–7

St Bernard's lily

Anthericum liliago

Delicate per to 60 cm. Lvs all basal, flat, 5 mm broad. Infl terminal, fls to 5 cm divided into 6 spread segs. *D:* C; *Fl:* 5–6

Wild tulip

Tulipa sylvestris

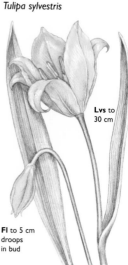

Lvs to 30 cm

Fl to 5 cm droops in bud

Glaucous bulbous per to 60 cm; 3 basal linear lvs. Fls erect, spreading, bell-shaped. *D:* C, S; *Fl:* 4–5

Spring squill

Scilla verna

Fl to 1.5 cm

Lvs to 20 cm

Bulbous per; infl 2–5 fls, bracts longer than fl stks. *Ht:* 20 cm; *D:* W coasts; *Fl:* 4–5

Autumn squill

S. autumnalis

Fl to 1.2 cm

Leaves to 15 cm appear after fls; infl 4–20 fls; no bracts. *Ht:* 20 cm; *D:* W; *Fl:* 7–9

Alpine squill

S. bifolia

Fl to 1.6 cm, col varies

Usually only 2 glossy linear lvs. Infl loose 2–8 fls. *Ht:* to 20 cm; *D:* C, S; *Fl:* 3–6

Bluebell

Hyacinthoides non-scripta

Bulbous per; narrow, channelled lvs. Fl stk to 50 cm, 1-sided infl droops slightly. Fls bell-shaped to 2 cm. *D:* W; *Fl:* 4–6

Lily of the valley

Convallaria majalis

Fl c. 8 mm

Lvs long-stkd

Rhizomatous per; lvs to 20 cm, elliptical. Infl 1-sided, 6–12 nodding fls. Fr a red, poisonous berry. *Ht:* 20 cm; *D:* T; *Fl:* 5–6

Fritillary

Fritillaria meleagris

Bulbous per to 50 cm; 3–6 narrow stem lvs; 1 or 2 nodding fls to 5 cm. *D:* C, W; *Fl:* 4–5

Ramsons ⬡

Allium ursinum

Lvs to 15 cm long, 5 cm broad

Garlic smell as all *Allium* spp. 2 broad lvs; ridged fl stk to 45 cm, no bulbils. *D:* T (not far N); *Fl:* 4–6

Round-headed leek

A. sphaerocephalon

⬡

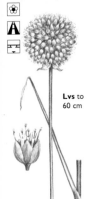

Lvs to 60 cm

Hollow lvs; dense infl no bulbils, 2 bracts, fls short-stkd. *Ht:* 60 cm; *D:* S; *Fl:* 6–8

Field garlic ✳

A. oleraceum

Fl bell-shaped

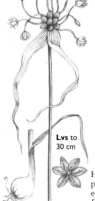

Lvs to 30 cm

Leaves hollow below. Infl of few fls, many bulbils and 2 bracts longer than fls. *Ht:* 60 cm; *D:* T; *Fl:* 7–8

Sand leek ✳

A. scordoprasum

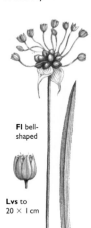

Fl bell-shaped

Lvs to 20 × 1 cm

Flat, linear lvs have rough edges. Infl has 2 bracts shorter than few fls, many bulbils. *Ht:* 60 cm; *D:* T (not N, SW); *Fl:* 5–8

Crow garlic ✳ 🅰

A. vineale

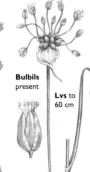

Bulbils present

Lvs to 60 cm

Hollow lvs; stamens protrude; 1 infl bract equals fls. *Ht:* 60 cm; *D:* T (not N); *Fl:* 6–7

Wild leek 🗻

A. ampeloprasum

Lvs to 40 × 2 cm

Strong ridge on lf underside, infl dense, few bulbils. 1 bract, soon falling. *Ht:* 1.5 m; *D:* W; *Fl:* 7–8

Chives

A. schoenoprasum

Wild leek

A. scordoprasum subsp rotundum

Fls short-stkd

Plant tussocky

Fl lobes spread

Leaves v narrow; infl dense, 2 bracts, no bulbils. *Ht:* 30 cm; *D:* T (local); *Fl:* 6–7

As *A. scordoprasum* (p. 162) but lf edges not rough or toothed. *Ht:* 30 cm; *D:* C, E; *Fl:* 6–8

Small grape hyacinth

Muscari botryoides

Grape hyacinth

M. neglectum

Tassel hyacinth

M. comosum

Fl 2 mm, globular

Fl 4 mm

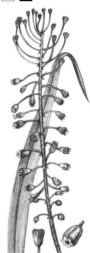

Linear lvs broader above, 2–4 per plant. Infl dense. *Ht:* 20 cm; *D:* S, C: Fl: 3–5

Leaves fine to 3 mm broad, 3–5 per plant. Infl long, dense, fls short-stkd. *Ht:* 17 cm; *D:* SW; *Fl:* 4–5

Leaves 1 cm broad; infl loose, fl stks v long, fls erect. *Ht:* 35 cm; *D:* S, C; *Fl:* 4–7

163

Meadow saffron

Colchicum autumnale

Linear lvs appear in spring, long-tubed fls in autumn. *Ht:* 25 cm; *D:* S, C; *Fl:* 8–10

Spiked star of Bethlehem

O. pyrenaicum

Linear lvs to 60 cm; infl of many fls all less than 1 cm, all fl stks equal length. *Ht:* to 1 m; *D:* SW; *Fl:* 6–7

Common star of Bethlehem

Ornithogalum angustifolium

Fl to 2 cm

Lvs to 30 cm

Narrow lvs; loose infl, 5–15 fls, longest stks on lowest fls, ptls free. *Ht:* 20 cm; *D:* T (not N); *Fl:* 4–6

Yellow star of Bethlehem

Gagea lutea

Single-hooded lf to 45 cm. Infl an umbel, 2–3 bracts at base, 1–5 fls. *Ht:* 45 cm; *D:* T (not N, W); *Fl:* 3–5

Drooping star of Bethlehem

O. nutans

Channelled leaves to 60 cm . Infl 1-sided, 2–12 large fls to 3 cm, stks all equal. *Ht:* 45 cm; *D:* S; *Fl:* 4–5

Gagea

G. arvensis

Two linear basal lvs; infl a loose umbel, 2 large hry bracts at base, fl stks hry, fls 3 cm diam. *Ht:* 25 cm; *D:* C, W; *Fl:* 2–4

Meadow gagea

G. pratensis

Bracts
equal fl stks

One v keeled basal lf;
infl 1–5 fls, 2 bracts at
base equal fl stks. *Ht:*
15 cm; *D:* E; *Fl:* 3–4

Belgian gagea

G. spathaca

Fl stks
hrlss

Has 2 v narrow basal
lvs. Infl 2–5 fls, 2
bracts. *Ht:* to 15 cm;
D: C, E; *Fl:* 4–5

Least gagea

G. minima

Has single, v narrow
basal lf. Infl 1–7 fls
with 2 basal bracts,
slim fl stks. *Ht:* to 45
cm; *D:* E; *Fl:* 3–5

Scottish asphodel

Tofieldia pusilla

Rhizomatous herb to
20 cm; lvs 3–5 veins,
stiff, erect; infl dense,
stks lflss, fls 2 mm.
D: N, S; *Fl:* 6–8

German asphodel

T. calyculata

As *T. pusilla* but infl
stk lfy, each fl has
unlobed and 3-lobed
bract. Plant robust. *Ht:*
20 cm; *D:* C, E; *Fl:* 7–8

Bog asphodel

Narthecium ossifragum

Rhizomatous, mat-
forming. Lvs strongly
flattened as *Iris* spp
(p. 168). Fl stk to
1 cm, 1 bract. *Ht:* 30
cm; *D:* W; *Fl:* 7–9

Asparagus officinalis

Lf-like brs
to 2 cm

Fl to
6 mm

Hairless herb to 1.5 m. Stems die back in winter. Brs lf-like, narrow, clustered. ♂, ♀ fls separate, 1 or 2 in lf axils. *D:* W coasts; *Fl:* 6–7

Whorled Solomon's seal

Polygonatum verticillatum

Has stout rhizome; stems v ridged. Lvs linear, 3–6 per whorl. Fls 1–4 per stk. *Ht:* 60 cm; *D:* T; *Fl:* 6–7

Herb Paris

Paris quadrifolia

Lvs 4 per whorl to 12 cm

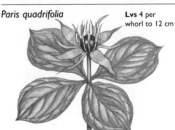

Rhizomatous, hrlss per to 40 cm. Fls 4 equal ptls and spls. Fr a black berry. *D:* T; *Fl:* 5–8

Solomon's seal

P. multiflorum

Fr black

Stems unridged to 80 cm. Lvs alt, unstkd. Fls to 1.5 cm, 2–5 per gp. *D:* T (not N); *Fl:* 5–6

Butcher's broom

Ruscus aculeatus

Fl 3 mm

Lf-like shs
to 4 cm

Erect, stiff evergreen to 80 cm. Shs lf-like, leathery, sharp points. ♂, ♀ fls separate on flat shs in axil of small bract. *D:* W; *Fl:* 1–4

Daffodil family Liliaceae (Amaryllidaceae)

Bulbous herbs. Flowers surrounded by a non-green bract (spathe) have petals in 2 whorls, the inner ones often trumpet-shaped. The ovary lies below the other flower parts.

Wild daffodil

Narcissus pseudonarcissus

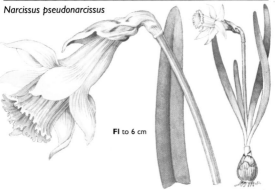

Fl to 6 cm

Erect glaucous lvs narrow, ridged. Fl stk to 35 cm; 2 ridges. Fl has trumpet equal in length to spread outer ptl whorl. *D:* W; *Fl:* 2–4

Summer snowflake | Spring snowflake

Leucojum aestivum | L. vernum

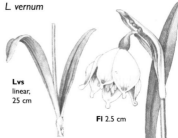

Lvs
linear,
25 cm

Fl 2.5 cm

Linear lvs; infl 3–5 fls each 1.5 cm, bract green-tipped. *Ht:* 45 cm; *D:* C; *Fl:* 4–5

Flowers sol, all ptls in 1 bell-shaped whorl, bract green at centre. *Ht:* 25 cm; *D:* C; *Fl:* 2–4

Snowdrop

Galanthus nivalis

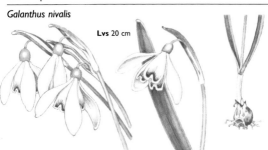

Lvs 20 cm

Linear lvs, outer ptl whorl to 1.7 cm, 2 × length of bell-shaped inner whorl. Bract 2-lobed, green at centre. *Ht:* 20 cm; *D:* C, S, W; *Fl:* 1–3

Iris family Iridaceae

Plants with linear sheathing leaves not divided into blades and stalks. Flowers have 6 petals in 2 whorls joined in a tube, 3 stamens and one or 2 bracts. The ovary is inferior.

Yellow iris

Iris pseudacorus

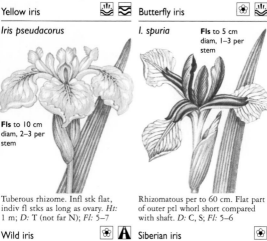

Fls to 10 cm diam, 2–3 per stem

Tuberous rhizome. Infl stk flat, indiv fl stks as long as ovary. *Ht:* 1 m; *D:* T (not far N); *Fl:* 5–7

Butterfly iris

I. spuria

Fls to 5 cm diam, 1–3 per stem

Rhizomatous per to 60 cm. Flat part of outer ptl whorl short compared with shaft. *D:* C, S; *Fl:* 5–6

Wild iris

I. aphylla

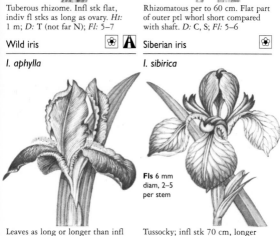

Leaves as long or longer than infl stk. Like garden iris (*I germanica*). *Ht:* 70 cm; *D:* EC; *Fl:* 5–6

Siberian iris

I. sibirica

Fls 6 mm diam, 2–5 per stem

Tussocky; infl stk 70 cm, longer than lvs. Bracts brown, outer ptls rounded at tip. *D:* C, E; *Fl:* 5–6

Stinking iris

I. foetidissima

Fl 8 cm diam

Strong-smelling, erect per to 80 cm. Lvs evergreen; infl stk ridged on 1 side, indiv fl stks 4 × ovary length, 2–3 fls per stem. *D:* W; *Fl:* 5–7

Sand crocus

Romulea columnae

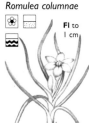

Fl to 1 cm

Very slim lvs longer than fl stk. 2 ptl whorls similar. *Ht:* 8 cm; *D:* W; *Fl:* 3–5

Spring crocus

Crocus vernus

Fl to 5 cm

Channelled lvs, white line in groove; ptls all sim, joined below. *Ht:* 7 cm; *D:* W; *Fl:* 3–5

Gladiolus

Gladiolus illyricus

Erect, hrlss to 90 cm. Lvs to 30 cm. Infl 1-sided spike, 2 lf-like bracts at base of each 3 cm fl, ptl tube short. *D:* W; *Fl:* 6–8

Blue-eyed grass

Sisyrinchium bermudiana

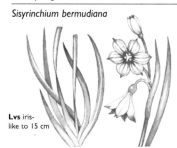

Lvs iris-like to 15 cm

Erect per to 45 cm. Infl of 2–4 fls each 1.5 cm diam, all ptls sim. *D:* C, W; *Fl:* 7

Yam family Dioscoreaceae

Herbaceous or woody climbers with rhizome tubers and spirally arranged leaves. Clustered bell-shaped flowers have 6 petals, 3 or 6 stamens and an inferior 3-celled ovary.

Black bryony

Tamus communis

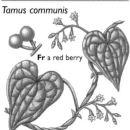

Fr a red berry

Clambers to 4 m. Lvs heart-shaped to 10 cm. ♂, ♀ fls axillary on separate plants, ♂ stkd, 6 stamens, ♀ unstkd. *D:* W; *Fl:* 5–7

Pipewort

Eriocaulon aquaticum

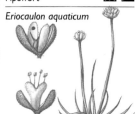

Flattened lvs translucent with evident cross-walls. Roots white sinuous. Twisted fl stems erect. Infl has grey bracts. *Ht:* 7–20 cm; *D:* W; *Fl:* 7–9

Orchid family Orchidaceae

Rhizomatous perennials forming close associations with root fungi. The unlobed leaves have parallel veins. Asymmetrical flowers in spikes are often large and showy. Similar sepals and petals form 6 flower segments: one back and 2 side sepals, 2 erect petals and one large central lip.

Lady orchid

Orchis purpurea

Infl dense

Lvs blunt

Leaves spotted. Fls have top lobes joined in helmet. Lip has 2 broad lobes. *Ht:* 30 cm; *D:* C, S; *Fl:* 5

Early purple orchid

O. mascula

Lip 3-lobed

Lvs to 20 cm

Blunt lvs, round dark blotches. Fl spur upcurved, long, thick. *Ht:* 45 cm; *D:* T (not far N); *Fl:* 4–6

Toothed orchid

O. tridentata

Fl lip spotted

Dense globular infl. Prominent fl lip, lobes round with central tooth. *Ht:* 20 cm; *D:* E; *Fl:* 3–5

Military orchid

O. militaris

Outer lip lobes shortest

Lvs blunt, no spots

Helmet grey and pink; outer fl lobes v pointed, lip lobes spread. *Ht:* 35 cm; *D:* C, S; *Fl:* 5–6

Monkey orchid

O. simia

As *O. militaris* but slim stems *c.* 20 cm. Pale helmet, white veins. Lip lobes narrow, linear, outer lobes longest. *D:* S, W; *Fl:* 5–6

Green-winged orchid

O. morio

Lvs to 9 cm

Helmet purple, green veins. Lip short, 3-lobed, spotted, spur straight. *Ht:* 25 cm; *D:* T (not N); *Fl:* 5–6

Loose-flowered orchid

O. laxiflora

Burnt orchid

O. ustulata

Bug orchid

O. coriophora

Lvs to 18 cm

Lvs pointed

Robust stems to 50 cm. Lvs narrow, pointed, lance-shaped. Fl lip has 2 big, round lobes. *D:* SW; *Fl:* 5–6

Spike dense, top buds dark purple, appearing burnt. Fl lip notched, spotted. *Ht:* to 20 cm; *D:* C, S; *Fl:* 5–6

Narrow lvs clasp stem. Infl dense, fls fetid, purple helmet green-veined. *Ht:* to 40 cm; *D:* C (local); *Fl:* 4–6

Pale-flowered orchid

Orchis pallens

Lip not spotted

Leaves widest nr tip. Fls yellow, lip darker, 3-lobed. *Ht:* 20 cm; *D:* C, S; *Fl:* 5–6

Fly orchid

Ophrys insectifera

Side ptls narrow, brown, velvety. Lip 3-lobed, centre lobe v notched. *Ht:* 45 cm; *D:* T (not N); *Fl:* 5–7

Bog orchid

O. laxiflora subsp *palustris*

As *O. laxiflora* (p. 171) but lip 3-lobed, centre lobe notched. *Ht:* 40 cm; *D:* SE, C; *Fl:* 5–6

Bee orchid

O. apifera

Flower lip large, patterned, bee-like, curled tooth beneath; spls pink. *Ht:* 30 cm; *D:* W, S; *Fl:* 6–7

False musk orchid

Chamorchis alpina

Fls greenish

Inconspicuous; lvs long, narrow. Lip not deeply lobed unlike *Herminium* (p. 174). *Ht:* 10 cm; *D:* N, S; *Fl:* 7–8

Late spider orchid

O. fuciflora

As *O. apifera* but lip flatter and broader than long, flat appendage at tip. *Ht:* 25 cm; *D:* C, S; *Fl:* 6–7

Early spider orchid

O. sphegodes

Spls
green-
yellow

As *O. fuciflora* but lip velvety, no appendage. *Ht:* to 45 cm; *D:* C, W, S; *Fl:* 4–6

Black vanilla orchid

Nigritella nigra

Lvs
numerous,
narrow

Ridged stem to 25 cm. Infl dense, conical, fls vanilla-scented. *D:* C, S; *Fl:* 6–8

Man orchid

Aceras anthropophorum

Lip lobes
narrow

Narrow infl, fls have red margins, lip man-shaped. *Ht:* 30 cm; *D:* W, S; *Fl:* 6–7

Lizard orchid

Himantoglossum hircinum

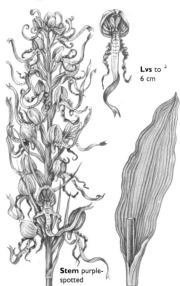

Lvs to
6 cm

Stem purple-spotted

Fetid fls, lip to 5 cm, 3-lobed; side lobes *c.* 1 cm, centre lobe flexuous. *Ht:* 30 cm; *D:* W, S; *Fl:* 5–7

Pyramidal orchid

Anacamptis pyramidalis

Basal lvs to 15 cm, stem lvs smaller; spur long, thin. *Ht:* 35 cm; *D:* T (not N); *Fl:* 6–8

Frog orchid | ## Lady's slipper orchid

Coeloglossum viride | ### *Cypripedium calceolus*

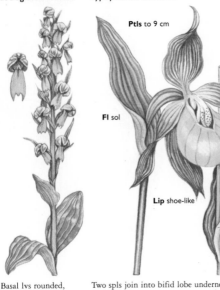

Ptls to 9 cm

Lvs oval

Fl sol

Lip shoe-like

Basal lvs rounded, blunt; lip oblong, tip 3-lobed, loose infl. *Ht:* 15 cm; *D:* T; *Fl:* 6–8

Two spls join into bifid lobe underneath curled, inflated lip. *Ht:* 35 cm; *D:* E, C; *Fl:* 5–6

Musk orchid

White frog orchid | ### Coralroot orchid

Herminium monorchis

Pseudorchis albida | ### *Corallorhiza trifida*

Infl delicate

Lip 3-lobed

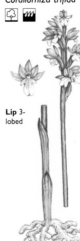

Slim, inconspicuous; 3 short, spread lip lobes. *Ht:* 10 cm; *D:* T (not N); *Fl:* 6–7

Glossy lvs; infl dense, columnar. Fls vanilla-scented, drooping, lip of 3 spread lobes. *Ht:* 20 cm; *D:* T; *Fl:* 5–7

No green pigment; has coral-like rhizome, scale lvs on stem, infl loose. *Ht:* to 25 cm; *D:* N, E; *Fl:* 5–8

Common spotted orchid Southern marsh orchid

Dactylorhiza fuchsii

D. praetermissa

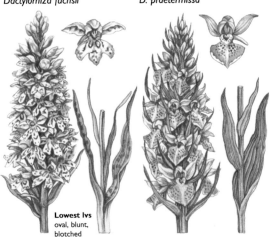

Lowest lvs oval, blunt, blotched

Lip has 3 almost equal lobes, centre lobe triangular, just largest. *Ht:* 17 cm; *D:* T (not NE); *Fl:* 6–8

Leaves unspotted. Infl dense, long bracts, lip slightly 3-lobed, spur robust. *Ht:* 45 cm; *D:* W; *Fl:* 6–8

Northern marsh orchid

D. purpurella

Fls deep purple

Early marsh orchid

D. incarnata

Heath spotted orchid

D. maculata

Lvs to 30 cm

Dense infl, purplish bracts; lip unlobed, diamond-shaped. *Ht:* 20 cm; *D:* NW; *Fl:* 6–7

Hollow stems to 50 cm; infl dense, big bracts. Lip margins bend back making lip look slim. *D:* T; *Fl:* 5–7

All lvs v pointed; 3-lobed lip, middle lobe smallest. *Ht:* to 50 cm; *D:* T; *Fl:* 6–8

Lesser butterfly orchid

Platanthera bifolia

Fl 1.5 cm diam, spur thin

Lvs to 9 cm

Slim cylindrical infl; lip a narrow tongue, spur straight. *Ht:* 25 cm; *D:* T; *Fl:* 5–7

Ghost orchid

Epipogium aphyllum

Lvs are scales

No green col; twisted fls, lip uppermost, spur vertical. *Ht:* 15 cm; *D:* C, N; *Fl:* 6–8

Greater butterfly orchid

P. chlorantha

Fl 2 cm

Loose, broad infl; lip narrow, spur long, curved. *Ht:* 30 cm; *D:* T (not far N); *Fl:* 5–7

Bog orchid

Hammarbya paludosa

Basal lvs to 1 cm

Slender stems to 12 cm, basal lvs round, have bulbils at edge; loose infl. *D:* C, N; *Fl:* 7–9

Fragrant orchid

Gymnadenia conopsea

Lvs lance-shaped

Slim, keeled lvs; fls frag, spur long, slim, curved. *Ht:* to 40 cm; *D:* T; *Fl:* 6–8

Fen orchid

Liparis loeselii

Bulbous, lvs v glossy; fls twisted, lip wavy, point upwards. *Ht:* 15 cm; *D:* C, E; *Fl:* 7

Calypso orchid

Calypso bulbosa

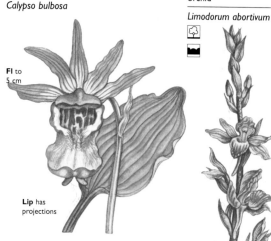

Fl to 5 cm

Lip has projections

Oval lvs *c.* 8 cm, prominent veins. Lip concave forming a "shoe", other ptls and spls erect, lip hry. *Ht:* 15 cm; *D:* N; *Fl:* 5–7

Violet birdsnest orchid

Limodorum abortivum

Stem robust

No green col. Hooded fls to 4 cm, spur long, down-pointed. *Ht:* 60 cm; *D:* T; *Fl:* 5–7

Birdsnest orchid

Neottia nidus-avis

No green pigment; lvs scale-like. Loose infl, lip large, 2-lobed at base. *Ht:* 35 cm; *D:* T (not N); *Fl:* 6–7

Creeping lady's tresses

Goodyera repens

Bracts long

Has stolons; lvs oval, stkd, net-veined in rosettes. Fls frag. *Ht:* 20 cm; *D:* N, mts in C, S; *Fl:* 7–8

Autumn lady's tresses

Spiranthes spiralis

Fls in 1 row

Leaves green, scale-like. Infl spirally twisted. *Ht:* 15 cm; *D:* T (not N); *Fl:* 8–9

Lesser twayblade

Listera cordata

Basal lvs in 1 opp pr, narrow at base. Lip reddish, 2-lobed, under 5 mm. *Ht:* 10 cm; *D:* N, C; *Fl:* 7–9

Common twayblade

L. ovata

Lvs to 20 cm

Basal lvs in 1 opp pr. Lip yellow-green, 2-lobed to 1.5 cm. *Ht:* 45 cm; *D:* T; *Fl:* 6–7

Red helleborine

Cephalanthera rubra

Spls pointed

Lvs pointed

Stem stickily hry above; fl longer than bracts. *Ht:* 35 cm; *D:* T (not N, NW); *Fl:* 6–7

White helleborine

C. damasonium

Lvs to 10 cm

Lip constricted in centre

Oval lvs. Fl parts much shorter than bracts, not spread, spls blunt. *Ht:* 35 cm; *D:* T (not N); *Fl:* 5–6

Narrow-leaved helleborine

C. longifolia

Fl parts not spread

Lvs to 20 cm

Pointed, lance-shaped lvs. Most fls longer than bracts, pointed spls. *Ht:* 45 cm; *D:* C, E; *Fl:* 5–7

Marsh helleborine   ## Broad-leaved helleborine

Epipactis palustris

E. helleborine

Lip jointed

Lvs broadly oval

Patch-forming with rhizome. Spls brown-purple, hry on outside. *Ht:* 30 cm; *D:* T (not N); *Fl:* 6–8

Leaves spirally arranged. Fls have large, round appendage over stigma. *Ht:* 65 cm; *D:* T (not N); *Fl:* 7–10

Dark red helleborine

Narrow-lipped helleborine

Green-flowered helleborine

E. atrorubens

E. leptochila

E. phyllanthes

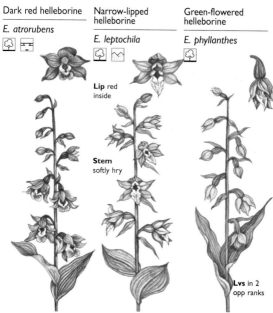

Lip red inside

Stem softly hry

Lvs in 2 opp ranks

Stem to 30 cm, dense soft hrs. Pointed lvs in opp ranks; fls red-purple all over. *D:* T (local in W); *Fl:* 6–7

Leaves in 2 opposite ranks; spread fl parts shorter than lowest bracts. *Ht:* 55 cm; *D:* C, W (local); *Fl:* 6–8

Stem to 45 cm, usually hrlss. Fls droop vertically from hrlss fl stk. Lip cup white inside. *D:* W; *Fl:* 7–9

Arum family Araceae

Herbs with small flowers crowded on to a club-shaped spadix and surrounded by a bract or spathe. Male flowers are in the upper spadix, female below with 4–6 petals.

Lords and ladies, Cuckoo pint

Arum maculatum

Hairless per to 25 cm. Lvs to 20 cm with dark green midrib, arise in spring. Spadix to 12 cm, half spathe length. *D:* T (not N); *Fl:* 4–5

Large cuckoo pint

A. italicum

Hairless per. Lvs to 30 cm with pale midrib, arise in winter (by Dec). Spadix ⅓ × spathe, yellow tip, spathe 35 cm. *D:* W; *Fl:* 4–5

Bog arum

Calla palustris

Lf blades emergent

Aquatic per to 30 cm. Lvs heart-shaped, spathe to 7 cm, flat, 2 × spadix. *D:* C, E; *Fl:* 6–8

Sweet flag

Acorus calamus

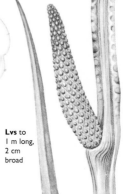

Lvs to 1 m long, 2 cm broad

Flower stk has lateral spadix to 8 cm and continues to lfy tip. *Ht:* 1 m; *D:* T (not far N); *Fl:* 5–7

Duckweed family Lemnaceae

Floating aquatics with leaf-like or disc-shaped stems from whose undersides roots and male and female flower buds arise.

Common duckweed | Greater duckweed

Lemna minor

Floating disc to 4 mm diam, flat on both sides, 1 unbranched rt usually c. 4 cm. D: T; Fl: 6–7

Spirodela polyrhiza

Disc to 8 mm, reddish below. Sev rts to 3 cm arise from underside centre. D: T (not N); Fl: 7

Ivy-leaved duckweed	Gibbous duckweed	Rootless duckweed

L. trisulca

Submerged; 3 discs held together in lobed plate to 1.2 cm. D: T (not far N); Fl: 5–7

L. gibba

Discs swollen, convex above and below to 5 mm; 1 unbranched rt. D: T (not N); Fl: 6–7

Wolffia arrhiza

Disc rtlss, egg-shaped to 1 mm, rarely fls. V much smaller than *Lemna* spp. D: C, S

Bur-reed family Sparganiaceae
Reedmace family Typhaceae

Perennial linear-leaved aquatics. Bur-reeds have globular inflorescences of single-sexed flowers. Reedmaces have a spadix with male flowers above, female flowers lower down.

Branched bur-reed	Unbranched bur-reed	Reedmace

Sparganium erectum

Lvs keeled to 1.5 cm broad

Branched infl, ♂ heads at branch tips, ♀ at bases. Ht: 1 m; D: T (not far N); Fl: 6–8

S.emersum

Erect or floating unbranched stems and lvs (keeled). ♂ heads at shoot apex. Ht: 20–60 cm; D: T; Fl: 6–7

Typha latifolia

Lvs to 2 cm wide

Broad lvs. ♂ part of infl directly over ♀. Ht: 2 m; D: T (not far N); Fl: 6–7

Lesser reedmace

T. angustifolia

Narrow lvs. Ht: 2.5 m; D: T (not far N); Fl: 6–7

Index

Entries in brackets are plants mentioned in the text but not described in full. English family names have been omitted but can be found by looking up the English names of the plants they cover. The entry 'pea', for example, will take you to the pea family.